THE BEDSIDE BOOK
of
IRISH GHOST STORIES

Collected and Edited
by

PATRICK F. BYRNE

THE MERCIER PRESS
DUBLIN and CORK

The Mercier Press Limited
4 Bridge Street, Cork
25 Lower Abbey Street, Dublin 1

© Patrick Byrne 1980

ISBN 0 85342 623 6

To my wife, Monica
who typed all my books and patiently endured
all the unexpected pitfalls involved,
I dedicate this book

Acknowledgements

The author and publisher would like to thank the following for permission to use their material:

Independent Newspapers Limited, Christopher Casson, Walter Curley, Michael Feeney, Patrick Murray, Brendan Price, Aidan Grennell. Also Sairseal agus Dill for 'The Girl in the High Heels' from *Gan Baistead* by Tomás Bairead, The Mercier Press for 'Strange Things in the Sky' from *A Place in the Sky* by Aidan Quigley, Colin Smythe for 'Strange Goings-on in Co. Mayo' from *Between Two Worlds* by Captain Dermott MacManus, RTE for 'The Ghosts of Rathgar' from *Sunday Miscellany* by Val Mulkerns and W. H. Allen for 'Steptoe's Ghostly Experience' from *All Above Board* by Wilfrid Brambell, and particularly Vincent Doyle for permission to quote material from the *Evening Herald's* Ghost column.

Contents

1. The White Cat of Drumgunniol

The traveller from Limerick to Dublin, having passed the hills of Killaloe upon the left, as the Keeper Mountain rises high in view, finds himself gradually hemmed in on the right by a range of lower hills. An undulating plain that dips gradually to a lower level than that of the road interposes, and some scattered hedgerows relieve its somewhat wild and melancholy character.

One of the few human habitations that send up their films of turf-smoke from that lonely plain, is the loosely-thatched, earth-built dwelling of a 'strong farmer', as the more prosperous of the tenant-farming classes are termed in Munster. It stands in a clump of trees near the edge of a wandering stream, about half-way between the mountains and the Dublin road, and had been for generations tenanted by people named Donovan.

In a distant place I had been inquiring for a teacher capable of instructing me in the Irish language, for I wanted to study some Irish records which had fallen into my hands. Mr Donovan, dreamy, harmless, and learned, was recommended to me for the purpose.

I found that he had been educated as a Sizar in Trinity College, Dublin. He now supported himself by teaching, and the special direction of my studies, I suppose, flattered his national partialities, for he unbosomed himself of much of his long-reserved thoughts, and recollections about his country and his early days. It was he who told me this story, and I mean to repeat it, as nearly as I can, in his own words.

'When I was a boy,' said he, 'living at home at Drumgunniol, I used to take my Goldsmith's *Roman History* in my hand and go down to my favourite seat, the flag stone, sheltered by a hawthorn tree beside the little lough, a large and deep pool. It lay in the gentle hollow of a field that is overhung towards the north by the old orchard, and being a deserted place was ideally quiet for my studies.

'One day reading here, as usual, I wearied at last, and began to look about me, thinking of the heroic scenes I had just been reading. I was wide awake and I saw a woman appear at the corner of the orchard and walk down the slope. She wore a long, light grey dress, so long that it seemed to sweep the grass behind her, and so singular was her appearance in a part of the world where female attire is so inflexibly fixed by custom, that I could not take my eyes off her. Her course lay diagonally from corner to corner of the field, which was a large one, and she pursued it without swerving.

'When she came near I could see that her feet were bare, and that she seemed to be looking steadfastly upon some remote object for guidance. Her route would have crossed me—had the lough not interposed—about ten or twelve yards below the point at which I was sitting. But instead of arresting her course at the margin of the lough, as I had expected, she went on without seeming conscious of its existence, and I saw her walk across the surface of the water, and pass, without seeming to see me, at about the distance I had calculated.

'I was ready to faint from sheer terror. I was only thirteen years old then, and I remember everything as if it had happened this hour.

'The figure passed through the gap at the far corner of the field, and there I lost sight of it. I had hardly strength to walk home, and was so nervous, and ultimately so ill, that for three weeks I was confined to the house, and could not bear to be alone for a moment. I never entered that field again, such was the horror with which from that moment every object in it was clothed. Even at this distance of time I should not like to pass through it.

'This apparition I connected with a mysterious event; and, also, with a singular liability, that has for nearly eighty years distinguished, or rather afflicted, our family. It is no fancy. Everybody in that part of the country knows all about it. Everybody connected what I had seen with it.

'About a year after the sight I had seen in the lough field, we were one night expecting my father home from the fair of Killaloe. My mother sat up to welcome him home, and I with her, for I liked nothing better than such a vigil. My brothers and sisters and the farm servants, except the men who were driving home the cattle from the fair, were asleep in their beds. My mother and I were sitting in the chimney corner chatting together, and watching my father's supper, which was kept hot over the fire. We knew he would return before the men who were driving home the cattle, for he was riding, and told us he would only wait to see them fairly on the road, and then push homeward.

'At length we heard his voice and the knocking of his loaded whip at the door, and my mother let him in. I don't think I ever saw my father drunk, which is more than most men of my age, from the same part of the country, could say of theirs. But he could drink his glass of whisky as well as another, and he usually came home from fair or market a little merry and mellow, and with a jolly flush in his cheeks.

'Tonight he looked sunken, pale and sad. He entered with the saddle and bridle in his hand, and he dropped them against the wall, near the door, and put his arms round his wife's neck, and kissed her kindly.

'"Welcome home, Michael," said she, kissing him heartily.

'"God bless you, mavourneen," he answered.

'And hugging her again, he turned to me, who was plucking him by the hand, jealous of his notice. I was little, and light of my age, and he lifted me up in his arms, and kissed me, and my arms being about his neck, he said to my mother: "Draw the bolt."

'She did so, and setting me down very dejectedly, he walked to the fire, sat down on a stool, and stretched his feet towards the glowing turf, leaning with his hands on his knees.

'"Rouse up, Mick, darling," said my mother, who was growing anxious, "and tell me how did the cattle sell, and did everything go lucky at the fair, or is there anything wrong with the landlord, or what in the world is it that ails you, Mick?"

'"Nothing, Molly. The cows sold well, thank God, and there's nothing fell out between me and the landlord, and everything's the same way. There's no fault to find anywhere."

"'Well, then, Mick, since so it is, turn round to your hot supper, and eat it, and tell us is there anything new."

"'I got my supper, Molly, on the way, and I can't eat a bit," he answered.

"'Got your supper on the way, and you knowing 'twas waiting for you at home, and your wife sitting up and all!' cried my mother, reproachfully.

"'You're taking a wrong meaning out of what I say," said my father. "There's something happened that leaves me that I can't eat a mouthful, and I'll not be dark with you, Molly, for, maybe, it is not very long I have to be here, and I'll tell you what it was. It's what I've seen, the white cat."

"'The Lord between us and harm!" exclaimed my mother, in a moment as pale and as chap-fallen as my father; and then, trying to rally, with a laugh, she said: "Ha! 'tis only funning me you are. Sure a white rabbit was snared last Sunday, in Grady's wood; and Teigue saw a big white rat in the haggard yesterday."

"'Twas neither rat nor rabbit was in it. Don't think but I'd know a rat or a rabbit from a big white cat, with green eyes as big as halfpennies, and its back raised up like a bridge, trotting on and across me, and ready, if I dared stop, to rub its sides against my shins, and maybe to make a jump and seize my throat, if that it's a cat, at all, and not something worse?"

'As he ended his description in a low tone, looking straight at the fire, my father drew his big hand across his forehead once or twice, his face being damp and shining with the moisture of fear, and he sighed or rather groaned, heavily.

'My mother had relapsed into panic, and was praying again in her fear. I, too, was terribly frightened, and on the point of crying, for I knew all about the white cat.

'Clapping my father on the shoulder, by way of encouragement, my mother leaned over him, kissing him, and at last began to cry. He was wringing her hands in his, and seemed in great trouble.

'"There was nothing came into the house with me?" he asked, in a very low tone, turning to me.

'"There was nothing, father," I said, "but the saddle and bridle that was in your hand."

'"Nothing white in at the door with me," he repeated.

'"Nothing at all," I answered.

'"So best," said my father, and making the sign of the cross, he began mumbling to himself, and I knew he was saying his prayers.

'Waiting for a while, to give him time for this exercise, my mother asked him where he first saw it.

'"When I was riding up the bohereen, I thought the men were on the road with the cattle, and no one to look to the horse barring myself, so I thought I might as well leave him in the crooked field below, and I took him there, he being cool, and not a hair turned, for I rode him easy all the way. It was when I turned, having let him go—the saddle and bridle being in my hand—that I saw it, pushing out of the long grass at the side of the path, and it walked across it, in front of me, and then back again, before me, the same way, and sometimes at one side, then at the other, looking at me with those shining eyes; and I swear I heard it growling as it kept beside me—as close as ever you see—till I came up to the door, here, and knocked and called, as you heard me."

'Now, what was it, in so simple an incident, that agitated my father, my mother, myself, and finally, every member of this rustic household, with a terrible foreboding? It was this that we, one and all, believed that my father had received, in thus encountering the white cat, a warning of his approaching death.

'The omen had never failed hitherto. It did not fail now. A week after my father took the fever that was going, and before a month he was dead.'

My honest friend, Dan Donovan, paused here; I could perceive that he was praying, for his lips were busy, and I concluded that it was for the repose of that departed soul.

In a little while he resumed.

'It is eighty years now since that omen first attached itself to my family. Eighty years? Yes, it is. Ninety is nearer the mark. And I have spoken to many old people from those earlier times, who had a distinct recollection of everything connected with it.

'It happened in this way.

'My grand-uncle, Connor Donovan, had the old farm of Drumgunniol in his day. He was richer than ever my father was, or my father's father either, for he took a short lease of Balraghan, and made money of it. But money won't soften a hard heart, and I'm afraid my grand-uncle was a cruel man—a profligate man he was, surely, and that is mostly a cruel man at heart. He drank his share, too, and cursed and swore, when he was vexed, more than was good for his soul,

13

I'm afraid.

'At that time there was a beautiful girl of the Colemans, up in the mountains, not far from Capper Cullen. I'm told that there are no Colemans there now at all, and that family has passed away. The famine years made great changes.

'Ellen Coleman was her name. The Colemans were not rich. But, being such a beauty, she might have made a good match. Worse than she did for herself, poor thing, she could not.

'Con Donovan — my grand-uncle, God forgive him! — sometimes in his rambles saw her at fairs or patterns, and he fell in love with her, as who might not?

'He used her ill. He promised her marriage, and persuaded her to come away with him; and, after all, he broke his word. It was just the old story. He tired of her, and he wanted to push himself in the world; and he married a girl of the Collopys, that had a great fortune—twenty-four cows, seventy sheep, and a hundred and twenty goats.

'He married this Mary Collopy, and grew richer than before; and Ellen Coleman died broken-hearted. But that did not trouble the strong farmer much.

'He would have liked to have children, but he had none, and this was the only cross he had to bear, for everything else went much as he wished.

'One night he was returning from the fair of Nenagh. A shallow stream at that time crossed the road—they have thrown a bridge over it, I am told, some time since—and its channel was often dry in summer weather. When it was so, as it passes close by the old farmhouse of Drumgunniol, without a great

14

deal of winding, it makes a sort of road, which people then used as a short cut to reach the house. Into this dry channel, as there was plenty of light from the moon, my grand-uncle turned his horse, and when he had reached the two ash-trees at the meering of the farm he turned his horse short into the river-field, intending to ride through the gap at the other end, under the oak-tree, and so he would have been within a few hundred yards of his door.

'As he approached the "gap" he saw, or thought he saw, with a slow motion, gliding along the ground towards the same point, and now and then with a soft bound, a white object, which he described as being no bigger than his hat. What it was he could not see, as it moved along the hedge and disappeared at the point to which he himself was tending.

'When he reached the gap the horse stopped short. He urged and coaxed it in vain. He got down to lead it through, but it recoiled, snorted, and fell into a wild trembling fit. He mounted it again. But its terror continued, and it obstinately resisted his caresses and his whip. It was bright moonlight, and my grand-uncle was chafed by the horse's resistance, and, seeing nothing to account for it, and being so near home, what little patience he possessed forsook him, and, plying his whip and spur in earnest, he broke into oaths and curses.

'All of a sudden the horse sprang through, and Con Donovan, as he passed under the broad branch of the oak, saw clearly a woman standing on the bank beside him, her arm extended. She struck him a blow upon the shoulders with her hand as he flew by. It threw him forward upon the neck of the horse, which, in wild terror, reached the door at a gallop, and stood there quivering and steaming all over.

'Less alive than dead, my grand-uncle got in. He told his story, at least, so much as he chose. His wife did not quite know what to think. But she could not doubt that something very bad had happened. He was very faint and ill, and begged that the priest should be sent for. When they were getting him to his bed they distinctly saw the marks of five fingerpoints on the flesh of his shoulder, where the spectral blow had fallen. These singular marks—which they said resembled in tint the hue of a body struck by lightning—remained imprinted on his flesh, and were buried with him.

'When he had recovered sufficiently to talk with the people about it—speaking, like a man at his last hour, from a burdened heart and troubled conscience—he repeated his story, but said he did not see, or, at all events, know, the face of the figure that stood in the gap. No one believed him. He told more about it to the priest than to others. He certainly had a secret to tell. He might as well have divulged it frankly, for the neighbours all knew well enough that it was the face of dead Ellen Coleman that he had seen.

'From that moment my grand-uncle never raised his head. He was a scared, silent, broken-spirited man. It was early summer then, and at the fall of the leaf in the same year he died.

'Of course there was a wake, such as beseemed a strong farmer so rich as he. For some reason the arrangements of this ceremonial were a little different from the usual routine.

'The usual practice is to place the body in the great room, or kitchen, as it is called, of the house. In this particular case the body was placed in a small room that opened upon the greater one. The door of this, during the wake, stood open. There were candles about the bed, and pipes and tobacco on the table, and stools for such guests as chose to enter, the door standing open for their reception.

'The body, having been laid out, was left alone, in this smaller room, during the preparations for the wake. After nightfall one of the women, approaching the bed to get a chair which she had left near it, rushed from the room with a scream, and, having recovered her speech at the further end of the "kitchen", and surrounded by a gaping audience, she said, at last:

'"May I never sin, if his face wasn't raised up against the back of the bed, and he staring down to the door, with eyes as big as pewter plates that would be shining in the moon!"

'"Arra, woman! Is it cracked you are?" said one of the farm boys as they are termed, being men of any age you please.

'"Agh, Molly, don't be talking, woman! 'Tis what you dreamt going into the dark room, out of the light. Why didn't you take a candle in your fingers, you fool?" said one of her female companions.

'"Candle, or no candle; I saw it," insisted Molly. "And what's more, I could almost take my oath I saw his arm, too, stretching out of the bed along the floor, three times as long as it should be, to take hold of me by the foot."

'"Nonsense, you fool, what did he want with your

foot?" exclaimed one scornfully.

'"Give me the candle, one of you—in the name of God," said old Sal Doolan, that was straight and lean, and a woman that could pray like a priest almost.

'"Give her a candle," agreed all.

'But whatever they might say, there wasn't one among them that did not look pale and stern enough as they followed Mrs Doolan, who was praying as fast as her lips could patter, and leading the van with a tallow candle, held like a taper, in her fingers.

'The door was half open, as the panic-stricken girl had left it; and holding the candle on high to examine the room better, she made a step or so into it.

'If my grand-uncle's hand had been stretched along the floor, in the unnatural way described, he had drawn it back again under the sheet that covered him. And tall Mrs Doolan was in no danger of tripping over his arm as she entered. But she had not gone more than a step or two with her candle aloft, when, with a drowning face, she suddenly stopped short, staring at the bed which was now fully in view.

'"Lord, bless us, Mrs Doolan, ma'am, come back," said the woman next to her, who had fast hold of her dress, drawing her backwards with a frightened pluck. A general recoil among her followers showed the alarm which her hesitation had inspired.

'"Quiet, will you?" said the leader, peremptorily, "I can't hear my own ears with the noise you're making, and which of you let the cat in here, and whose cat is it?" she asked, peering suspiciously at a white cat that was sitting on the breast of the corpse.

'"Put it away, will you?" she resumed, with horror

at the profanation. "Many a corpse as I stretched and crossed in the bed, the likes of that I never seen yet. The man of the house, with a brute beast like that mounted on him, like a phooka, Lord forgive me for naming the like in this room. Drive it away, some of you! Out of that, this minute, I tell you."

'Each repeated the order, but no one seemed inclined to execute it. They were crossing themselves, and whispering their conjectures and misgivings as to the nature of the beast, which was no cat of that house, nor one that they had ever seen before. Suddenly the white cat placed itself on the pillow over the head of the body, and having from that place glared for a time at them over the features of the corpse, it crept softly along the body towards them, growling low and fiercely as it drew near.

'Out of the room they bounced, in dreadful confusion, shutting the door fast after them, and not for a good while did the hardiest venture to peep in again.

'The white cat was sitting in its old place, on the dead man's breast, but this time it crept quietly down the side of the bed, and disappeared under it, the sheet which was spread like a coverlet, and hung down nearly to the floor, concealing it from view.

'Praying, crossing themselves, and not forgetting a sprinkling of holy water, they peeped, and finally searched, poking spades, "wattles", pitchforks and such implements under the bed. But the cat was not to be found, and they concluded that it had made its escape among their feet as they stood near the threshold. So they secured the door carefully, with hasp and padlock.

'But when the door was opened the next morning they found the white cat sitting, as if it had never been disturbed, upon the breast of the dead man.

'The same scene again occurred with a like result, only that some said they saw the cat afterwards lurking under a big box in a corner of the outer-room, where my grand-uncle kept his leases and papers, and his prayer-book and beads.

'Mrs Doolan heard it growling at her heels wherever she went; and although she could not see it, she could hear it spring on the back of her chair when she sat down, and growl in her ear, so that she would bounce up with a scream and a prayer, fancying that it was on the point of taking her by the throat.

'And the priest's boy, looking round the corner, under the branches of the old orchard, saw a white cat sitting under the little window of the room where my grand-uncle was laid out and looking up at the four small panes of glass as a cat will watch a bird.

'The end of it was that the cat was found on the corpse again, when the room was visited, and do what they might, whenever the body was left alone, the cat was found again in the same ill-omened contiguity with the dead man. And this continued, to the scandal and fear of the neighbourhood, until the door was opened finally for the wake.

'My grand-uncle being dead, and, with all due solemnities, buried, I have done with him. But not quite yet with the white cat. No banshee ever yet was more inalienably attached to a family that this ominous apparition is to mine. But there is a difference. The banshee seems to be animated with an affectionate sympathy with the bereaved family to whom it is hereditarily attached, whereas this thing has about it a suspicion of malice. It is the messenger simply of death. And its taking the shape of a cat—the coldest, and as they say, the most vindictive of brutes—is indicative of the spirit of its visit.

'When my grandfather's death was near, although he seemed quite well at the time, it appeared not exactly, but very nearly in the same way in which I told you it showed itself to my father.

'The day before my Uncle Teigue was killed by the bursting of his gun, it appeared to him in the evening, at twilight, by the lough, in the field where I saw the woman who walked across the water, as I told you. My uncle was washing the barrel of his gun in the lough. The grass is short there, and there is no cover near it. He did not know how it approached but the first he saw of it, the white cat was walking close round his feet, in the twilight, with an angry twist of its tail, and a green glare in its eyes, and do what he would, it continued walking round and round him, in larger or smaller circles, till he reached the orchard, and there he lost it.

'My poor Aunt Peg—she married one of the O'Brians, near Oolah—came to Drumgunniol to go to the funeral of a cousin who died about a mile away. She died herself, poor woman, only a month after.

'Coming from the wake, at two or three o'clock in the morning, as she got over the stile into the farm of Drumgunniol, she saw the white cat at her side. It kept close beside her, she ready to faint all the time, till she reached the door of the house, where it made a spring up into the white-thorn tree that grows close by, and so it parted from her. And my little brother Jim saw it also, just three weeks before he died. Every member of our family who dies, or takes his death-sickness, at Drumgunniol, is sure to see the white cat, and no one of us who sees it need hope for long life after.'

This story is by Joseph Sheridan Le Fanu

2. The Hanging Tree

For well over a hundred years apparitions have allegedly appeared a few hundred yards off the main Liscarroll-Charleville road just before some national catastrophe.

The first known account of the phenomenon was given back in 1848. On 10 July of that year a local farmer, Geoffrey Collins, assisted by his workman was driving cattle to the monthly fair at Liscarroll. The last wisps of the grey dawn were just disappearing from the sky chased by a bright sun which began peering over the hills and tree-tops, giving promise of a warm summer's day.

Nothing broke the silence of the picturesque countryside except the lowing of the cattle and the chatty twittering of the birds in the bushes. The two men hadn't as yet warmed sufficiently to break into a prolonged conversation and Mr Collins quietly puffed on his pipe in an effort to shake off some of the chilliness of the crisp air.

Suddenly, on nearing the spot where the 'Hanging Tree' stood, the men froze in their tracks for a series of spine-chilling cries rent the air. Even the cattle stopped their lowing, then put their tails on their backs and stampeded down the road.

Collins, having instructed his man to follow the terrified animals, quickly crossed the over-grown ditch and pushed his way in among the trees, which grew in abundance beyond.

The screams were coming from a hollow just below

him. The sight that met his eyes paralysed him and the short stubby pipe dropped from his open mouth to the dew-laden grass at his feet.

Walking around an old, gnarled tree in the centre of the depression were a number of women and men. It seemed that some terrible calamity had befallen them for they were wailing, shaking their heads and wringing their hands. Apart from that the odd thing, which struck the farmer, was the clothes the people were wearing for they were all clad in costumes which had been in vogue a century previously.

The astounded farmer stood rooted to the ground for a few moments, then, when he had mustered his courage sufficiently, he moved forward to the brink of the hollow. At the base of the tree lay what appeared to be a stretcher on which a child, covered with an old shawl, reposed.

At first he just could not believe his eyes and was so fascinated by the spectacle that unconsciously he moved nearer as if drawn by a magnet. His eyes had not deceived him: there was no doubt about it, although the figures seemed as solid as any living being, they were transparent.

He was now only about thirteen or fourteen feet away from them. He was amazed at his own courage for by right he should have fled from the eerie place as fast as he could but the macabre scene held him in a trance.

He counted the figures. There were five women, two of whom seemed to be in their 'teens, five children, including the one on the stretcher, and three men.

Although Collins was now almost in their midst,

they paid no attention to him but continued to walk, as if on air, around the tree. As they passed the stricken boy, they lifted their hands to the heavens and raised their keening much louder. The boy seemed about seven or eight years of age with the pallor of death spread over his small, pinched-up face. His big brown eyes held the terrified look of one who has witnessed some dreadful experience.

At last Collins was able to drag himself away and he turned his back on the spectacle and headed towards the road. Just before he recrossed the ditch, he gave one final glance back at the hollow, but it only added to his horror for the place was deserted — not a trace remained of the ghostly assembly.

Hurrying as fast as he could to Liscarroll, the farmer made straight for the police station and reported the matter to the man in charge: Constable Timothy Sugrue, who entered the extraordinary account in the day-book. The constable also advised Collins to inform the parish priest of his experience.

Investigations proved that the hollow and its old, weather-beaten tree had an historical connection, a bloody and barbaric one.

Following the Battle of Wexford in 1798, a group of refugees fleeing from the terrible aftermath were making a long and dangerous trek to the comparative safety of the Kerry mountains, when they were forced to shelter in the hollow in the wood just off the Liscarroll-Charleville road.

Yeomen and dragoons were combing the countryside for rebels and their sympathisers, who were shot or hanged on sight, so that travelling by day was a hazardous undertaking. The refugees were also handicapped with trying to carry a very sick boy, who could not stand up to the rigours of the journey.

On the night of 7 July, 1798, their hiding place in the hollow was discovered by the British soldiers, who surrounded the place and waited until the next morning to attack. No prisoner was taken; instead the unfortunate people were subjected to terrible tortures before being put out of their dreadful agony by being hanged from the tree.

The abortive rebellion of 1848 took place fifty years later, shortly after their phantom forms had appeared to James Collins. It ended in the capture of John Mitchell and his companions. They were tried, sentenced and deported to Van Diemen's Land.

On 18 February, 1867, the *Cork Daily Reporter* carried the following amazing story headed: 'Ghostly Happenings near Cork-Limerick Border':

'Before the Irish Parliamentary Party was unfortunately split by the Parnell crisis, the apparitions were seen again. *The Freeman's Journal* carried a long report of the phenomenon being seen by two farm hands, who were passing the hollow on their way to milking cows.

'Do the ghosts of the Liscarrol "Hanging Tree" really exist? The answer must remain a mystery but let us in all honesty say that the reports of such reliable witnesses during the last hundred years or so are not easily discounted.'

The story was written by Michael Feeney in the **Evening Herald.**

3. Shades of James Joyce

A few short years ago I was a student of James Joyce's works. I was studying along with four others, another Dubliner, a Londoner, a Kerryman and a Waterfordman. All were avid students of Joyce. It would be honest to say that we knew Joyce; we knew, by then, how he thought, how he felt, how he lived.

It came to the anniversary of Joyce's death. We all knew it was that day and really thought no more about it. However, one of our number, St John, had been reading about seances and as we were boarding in a school at the time, in our final year, he suggested that we hold a seance to try to contact Joyce on his deathday.

The other four of us scorned the idea, at first. But we eventually agreed to make a genuine effort, at two o'clock in the morning in the reading room.

It must have been after two when the five assembled. We laid out the letters of the alphabet around a circular table and we placed a glass, right way up, in the centre of the table. We all placed one finger on the glass. Before we began, each one of us was asked to try and move the glass with the other four remaining motionless.

It was impossible. Each time I tried to move it — it fell over. The same happened when the others tried. So we turned on a tape recorder, in case sounds we did not hear turned up.

We sat motionless and silent for hours. We neither spoke to each other nor did anything except repeat aloud the name Joyce.

At about quarter to four the glass moved towards St John. It was in between letters and it was like a hint. St John eventually spoke.

'Where are you?' he asked.

The glass moved — it moved firmly. It moved to specific letters.

'I cannot see God' it spelled out.

None of us reacted visibly. It was a few minutes before St John spoke again.

'What have you to say to us?' he asked.

'Say nothing of this to anyone' the glass replied.

We said nothing.

'I like you' it spelled out.

The English boy spoke.

The glass lifted about eighteen inches into the air; it fell on to the table and then on to the floor. It did not break. We sat motionless for a further hour. Then we replayed the tape. It revealed nothing.

We got up to leave. We said a few things of no consequence to each other and went to bed.

The next day at lunchtime we returned to the room. We again tried to move the glass by foul means. In fact, we tried two at a time to move it, with the other three motionless — but it fell over. We could not lift it off the table — even with all five trying. We never tried again. We did not speak much of the incident. We kept on asking each other — as we still do — if anyone cheated.

But no one did.

I would never return to that room in the school. That night in 1970 scared me. I try to believe it was a hoax — we all do.

But it is difficult.

A glass cannot be made to jump in the air when one's fingers are resting on the rim!

This story was told to me by Dublin journalist, Patrick Murray

4. The Strange Warner

What a night it was. The wind came, not in sudden gusts but in one continuous onrush that seemed as if it must, perforce, blow down all before it.

Coming as it did over an unbroken reach of sixty miles of Irish Sea, it appeared to have gained additional force and momentum with each mile of its way, and to launch the whole power of its fury against the first obstacle it met; wherefore the lighthouse seemed at times not only to oscillate, but absolutely to bend before its force; and when a wave caught up by the wind some hundred yards out, and borne along with swelling force, struck against it, the shock occasioned to the slender tower seemed for the moment to complete its overthrow.

Looking out over the wild waste of sea from the top, if there had been anybody there to look out, which there was not, save the lighthouse-keeper, the night would have presented itself as one of intense darkness, through which the feeble rays of the lighthouse lanterns were as pale specks, almost quenched by the surrounding gloom. There was no light on the land; there was no star in the sky; and, save the white crests of the waves rolling fiercely inwards, there was nothing to break the black wall of night and gloom that had built itself up around the lighthouse tower.

But if there were no stars in the lightless sky, there were two very bright particular stars in the comfortable chamber of the lighthouse; not fixed stars either, but moving and changing repeatedly, and sparkling with such radiant light and beauty as never yet shone from celestial star, fixed or wandering; for they were the two blue eyes in Nelly Williams' handsome face, which shone and twinkled with rare good humour as she sat at her work, polishing reflectors that seemed but the reflex of happy and pleasant thoughts. At times, indeed, they grew grave and serious, and even a little awestruck, as she lifted her head and glanced out through the little oval window opposite her, and listened to the moaning wind, as it swept from the Irish Sea upon the coast in more than usually stormy bursts.

Nelly did not usually reside at the tower, but she rowed over from the mainland with a message to her father this day, and the storm coming on unexpectedly she had to remain for the night. With a happy disposition to make the best of everything, she accepted the inevitable; and as her busy hands required something to occupy them, she had industriously sought to pass the time by aiding her father in the work.

Beside her—not quite beside, indeed, but in front of the fire that burned and blazed cheerfully on the hearth, fanned into flame by the draughts that came under the door—was a tall, active-looking young fellow in sailor's garb, who usually acted as assistant in the lighthouse.

I say usually, for in the summer time, and when there were no storms to be feared, the keeper dispensed with his services and lived alone; and then his assistant took himself to fishing in the neighbourhood, or doing other jobs, in the former of which he had for his companion the young girl now at work near him—for Nelly was born by the waves of the Irish Sea, where they pour into the turbid waters of Dublin Bay, and had all a Viking's love for the glancing waters. Whatever friendship existed between the two on these occasions—and it must have been by no means small—it was clear from the look of sullen pain and displeasure that now sat on his face, and his fixed glance, in avoidance of her, into the fire, that something unpleasant had grown up between them—if not on her side, certainly on his.

'It's a wild night, Eph,' said the young girl at last, breaking the silence, and turning around with a smiling glance at her morose companion.

'Aye, it is,' he replied coldly.

'And it isn't likely to be better tonight. Hear that!' she cried, not without a tinge of anxiety in her voice, as a huge wave came thundering against the walls.

'It's nearly as bad as the night when David Jones's ship came on the rocks, and your brother Oliver was drowned. It's just as bad, and —'

'Oh, Eph, don't mention that now,' pleaded the girl, somewhat startled. 'Please don't.'

'Why? What harm is there in it?' he asked, sharply.

'No harm, Eph; but—it frightens me. Don't you know that my brother Frank and Willie Strafford are off the coast by this? *The Dalkey Pride* will be rounding Lambay, and it's not pleasant to be talking of what happened then.'

'You're always thinking of Willie Strafford, Nelly,' said the young fellow, with angry warmth, turning to address her. 'It's always Willie Strafford with you now—never anyone else.'

'Well, and why wouldn't it?' she asked, cheerily,

the rose-tints which had fled at the mention of the shipwreck coming back to her face, and the merry sparkles in her eyes as the name occurred. 'Why would I? Who has a better right to speak of him?'

'It used not to be so. It's only lately he's come to be so much thought of.'

'Well, and what matter?' said Nelly pleasantly. 'What harm is it doing to anybody?'

'It is—it is doing harm,' he said, surlily.

'To whom? Who could it do harm to?' she asked with some surprise.

'To me.'

'To you, Eph?' cried Nelly, with a half-shriek, and nearly letting the reflector drop from her hands.

'Ay, to me, Nelly,' said he vehemently. 'I know you longer than he does, and I liked you before he did, and you loved me before he came. I know you did.'

'Eph, what are you talking of?' she queried indignantly. 'I know you a long time—ever since we were children, Eph—and I liked you then, and I like you still—why shouldn't I?—but—'

'But what, Nelly? But what? Go on, and say what you were going to say.'

'But—it wasn't in the same way that I like him,' answered Nelly, with evident embarrassment and reluctance, and a confusion that sent the blood mounting to her white temples. 'There now! Don't let us talk of it again.'

'It's easy for you to say, "Don't talk of it," Nelly —but what am I to do? I loved you before he saw you; I love you still—and now you cast me off like—'

'Ephraim, you mustn't talk like this,' she said, in

33

great distress, 'you must not, indeed. What is the use of complaining of what can't be helped. If Willie Strafford hadn't come, things might have been different, but I liked you better than all the world but him. I couldn't help myself, Eph—I couldn't help myself. What girl can? I could no more help myself loving him that I could the gale blowing outside.'

'You showed liking enough for me before he came,' repeated her companion gloomily, as if he had not heard a word, and indeed it was probable he had not, of her passionate statement.

'And I do still; I like you better than all the rest—except him,' said Nelly, in a pleading, distressed manner. 'If he hadn't come—'

'I wish he hadn't,' muttered her companion, in angry recklessness. 'I wish he may never—'

'Oh, Eph,' cried Nelly shocked, then, lowering her voice, 'See! here's father.'

The unpleasant conversation immediately ceased, for at this juncture the door leading to the stairs mounting upwards opened, and the lighthouse-keeper, lamp in hand, entered.

'It's an awful night aloft, Eph,' said the keeper, as drenched with the spray the wind bore in through the air slits in the tower, he took his seat in front of the blazing fire. 'It's worse than the night of the great storm almost.'

'I hope there'll be no wrecks this time,' said Ephraim, with sullen indifference.

'I hope not,' said the old keeper, with a heavy sigh. 'I hope not. Poor Oliver! 'Twas that night he was drowned. Oh, me!—the night of the great storm.'

'But he died in a good cause, father,' said Nelly,

comfortingly, for she knew what great sorrow it was to him whenever he referred to it—which was seldom. 'He died to save the lives of others—of brother sailors and Dublin men, out on the great waters.'

'But he needn't, Nelly—only through my fault, he needn't,' said the keeper, fretfully.

'You're fault, father?' cried Nelly in astonishment.

'Ay, Nelly—my fault—I never told it till now, and I don't know what makes me tell it now. But—the lights were out that night!'

'Out!' repeated his daughter, in a low voice filled with astonishment, while Eph turned with equal wonder to glance into his face.

'Out, Nelly—they were indeed! Sam Hellings—you remember when he was assistant here?—I left the lighting of the lamps that night to him, but he didn't know how, or was careless, or something, and they went out, or were never lit; and so *The Pearl of Dalkey* missed the channel, came in on the rocks, and poor Oliver lost his life trying to save the lives of those on board. He only came over here that day, but couldn't get back, just as you did today. He never did go back with his life, poor boy. I am sorry you came today, Nelly.'

'I am very glad I did, father,' said Nelly, drying her eyes, into which the tears welled with the sad recollection, 'for I like to be near you when there's trouble over you. But, father, what would have made Sam Hellings put out the lights?—or did he put them out?'

'I don't know, Nelly. Maybe he didn't know how to light them. But he said he did, and I left them to his care.'

'Oh, poor Oliver!' cried Nelly, involuntarily, whilst

a shudder passed through her. 'That was the reason Sam Hellings went away so suddenly.'

'That was the reason, Nelly. He went away the next morning, when he saw the mischief that was done, and saw poor Oliver's dead body on the rocks. He was sorry enough, broken-hearted, but what good could that do? It was all my fault, Nelly. I ought to have looked after them myself. It was easy to miss the channel when they could not see the lights; it would be a miracle if they didn't.'

'Well, father, don't you think of it longer; you did it for the best,' said his daughter, 'and you're not to blame that the sorrow came to us. 'Twas the will of God. But,' she added, after a pause, 'I hope they are all right now, father?'

'They're all right tonight, Nelly. I wouldn't trust them to anyone's hands but my own of a stormy night since,' said the keeper. 'It's a dangerous place, this Howth Head, and no ship could make the channels in the night if the lights were not seen—particularly in such a storm as this.'

This satisfied Nelly, whose mind at once reverted to the brother and lover who were coming into harbour from their long voyage; but she wisely kept her thoughts to herself, not to awaken apprehension in her father's mind.

Ephraim, the assistant, who had listened with keen interest to their conversation, and impressed probably by what he had heard, shook off his surly and sullen humour, and, after some time, taking the keeper's lamp in his hand, volunteered to go aloft and make certain that all was still right, and that the gale—if anything increasing in intensity—had not blown any of the lamps out. The keeper for a moment glanced at him in surprise, for he was not usually interested in his work, and nodded a pleasant acquiescence.

Father and daughter, when he had departed, still continued to discuss in a low tone the sad remembrance, but the old man was tired and weary with his exertions of the afternoon; the monotonous roar of wind and sea had a drowsy effect, and by degrees the conversation lapsed, and he fell asleep in his chair before the fire. The minutes and the quarter-hours passed away with ceaseless uncontrol until Nelly was aroused from them suddenly by the voice of her father as he started from his seat.

'Who calls? Who spoke?' he exclaimed, breaking the still silence of the little room, and startling her immeasurably. 'Was there anyone calling, Nelly?'

'No father,' said Nelly, 'there was no one calling —there was no sound in the room. You have been only dreaming. Sleep again and rest yourself. You are tired.'

'I suppose I was dreaming, Nelly; but I thought I heard someone calling—and, now that I think of it, it was Sam Helling's voice that seemed to call me!'

'God bless us!' cried his daughter in involuntary alarm, 'don't say that.'

'It was only dreaming I was,' explained the keeper, seeing how he had alarmed her. 'I'll go to sleep again. Ephraim will see that the lights are kept burning,' and, resuming his seat, was again soon sunk in sleep. But he had not long to repose; and he awoke with a renewed start, caused this time, however, not by a fancied voice calling, but by a burst of storm.

'Good heavens! It's a dreadful night; that's an awful storm, Nelly! I never heard the like of that before. Listen to it.'

A cry of terror came in answer to his exclamation—a cry that, in the apartment at least, overbore the noise of the storm—and, glancing round, the keeper beheld his daughter leaning back in her chair, her lips wide apart, her face perfectly colourless, and her eyes fixed with fascinating stare on the little window, whose thick glass gave on the raging seas and black night outside. It was little wonder that Nelly's usually rosy face should have lost its hue, and her eyes their sparkling light; for, whilst he slept, the wind had suddenly lifted itself above its previous level of fierceness, and came with such sustained and overwhelming force that it seemed as if nothing built by human hands could withstand it; and it did, indeed, appear as if the lighthouse must snap across before it. The lighthouse-keeper stayed his steps for a moment, and waited as if rooted to the floor, for the crash that he thought must come. But the hands that built the tower had done sound work, for the outburst passed over, and the angel of destruction swept by on the shrieking wind, leaving it unshaken.

'That was an awful blast. God be around us, Nelly,' said he, when his suspended breathing came back, and he was able to approach her and speak. 'You got a great fright, and so did I. But it's all over now, and no harm done. Don't be frightened, Nelly. The stone and mortar that could stand that would stand anything. Why, what are you afraid of? The height of the storm is over and gone. It cannot blow harder than that, come what may. Nelly! Nelly!—rouse yourself!

Skies above! She has fainted.'

The young girl had indeed partly swooned. The pallid face and staring eyes might, had he had more experience, have shown him this at first; but the changeless attitude and the heavy drops of dew forming on her temples demonstrated it to him now unmistakably.

'Nelly! Nelly!' he called, shaking her hurriedly by the shoulder, 'waken, rouse yourself! The worst of the storm is over and gone, and—'

The keeper was himself alarmed; but, to his great relief, his daughter opened her eyes and looked around. His last words had caught her ear.

'Gone! Is he gone? Oh, father, it was frightful! Say that he—that it is gone.'

'That he is gone! That who is gone?' queried the keeper, in fresh surprise. 'There has been no one here but me, Nelly—me, and the burst of storm that frightened you—that's all.'

'Oh, father, stay near me and protect me!' cried the shivering girl. 'Where's Eph? Oh! Father, keep near me—put your arms round me—for—I saw him!'

'Saw him, Nelly?' said the keeper, in increasing wonderment. 'How could you see him? He's gone aloft, and is not a step nearer than the top of the tower now. You're a little goose, Nelly, or you wouldn't talk so.'

'Father—I saw him—Sam Hellings—looking in at me through the window!' she cried.

'Sam Hellings!' the keeper said, for a moment rather startled.

He was by no means a nervous or easily frightened man, but the introduction of this name so soon after his own dream, and the evident look of terror in his daughter's face caused him no small surprise. But he shook it off at once.

'Why, no living thing could stand outside—even if there was standing room, which there is not—on such a night as this. You have been dreaming as well as I, Nelly. Or rather,' he continued after a pause, 'it was my nonsensical dream that put it into your head.'

'But I saw him, father!' cried his daughter, 'looking in at me, warning like, for a minute, and then he was gone.'

'Nelly, don't be foolish; don't you know that no living creature could be there! The gale again!' he cried, as the hurricane which had died out somewhat, as if exhausted after its recent outburst, put forth its powers afresh, as if determined once and for all to try and see if the lighthouse tower would not go down before its assaults. But in the midst of it the girl's cry came again on his ears—

'Father! father! close the shutter. It's there again! —looking in—see!'

The terrified girl could say no more. The keeper, with a strong effort stepped over to the window. It was a small, oval one, with a heavy iron shutter, which latter was seldom used, for the thick glass was strong enough to stand usual storms, and the wind was now beating against it. He bent his eyes keenly on the window as he approached it, in order that he might see what it was she saw, or thought she saw.

There was nothing there; but, as he closed the shutter, he paused for a moment. The crest of a wave, milk-white, churned into creamy foam by the storm, swept by. It was an unusual height for a wave to reach, and it looked in strange uncanny contrast with the impenetrable gloom beyond. For a moment he shrank instinctively back, and his hand forsook the shutter as the foam seemed, in the instant of vision, to assume to itself some of the lineaments of the human face; but the moment after, ashamed of his temporary want of courage, he closed and fastened it.

'Nelly, I know what it was!' he cried, in a burst of relief. 'The waves are flying white past the window. It was these you saw. I thought at first they were something else, myself. 'Twas these that frightened you —these, and nothing else.'

'O, father, I—'

'Don't be a goose, Nelly. 'Twas only the waves and the foam. Here's Ephraim, and he'll tell you the same thing.'

Eph, lamp in hand, entered. If Nelly were to seek courage from his appearance she was not likely to get it, for he, too, was deadly pale and haggard, and it was clear that the magnitude of the storm had affected him considerably. His hand trembled, and the light danced in his grasp as if it were in a chopping sea. But the lighted apartment and the presence of the keeper and his daughter seemed to restore him.

'It's all right aloft,' he said, with a strong attempt at conquering his trembling fit.

They drew their chairs over to the fire, placing Nelly, whose terror had much subsided at her father's explanation, between them for protection. It was not a time for much conversation, with the violence of the wind and sea outside, but the two men tried to keep chatting.

Presently Nelly interrupted, laying her hand on her

father's arm, and said—

'Hush! Listen! What is that!'

'What is what, Nelly?' he asked, petulantly. 'The storm! I've been hearing and listening to it for hours, you little fool.'

'It isn't that, father,' she said, still listening intently. 'It's the gun.'

'The gun! What gun!' he queried, angrily.

'The signal gun. A ship's in distress. Listen!' was the reply.

They all listened. There was dead silence for a second or two. But, save the hollow sound of the wind or the leaping waves breaking with heavy thud against the walls, no sound came to their ears.

'You must be mistaken, Nelly; there's no sound but the storm,' said her father, breaking the pause.

'There,' cried Nelly, eagerly, half-starting from her seat, 'there it is again! There's a ship in the breakers. Take care the lights are not out! Do you not hear it!'

'The lights are not out,' said Eph, in anger. 'Did I not just come down from them?'

'No, of course not—how could they,' said her father, confidently. 'But there's the gun, sure enough. There's a vessel in distress somewhere. Let us go up and see.'

They ascended to the next floor, ordinarily used as a bedroom. Here there was perfect darkness, but the window looked out on the sea, and the absence of light enabled them to survey the scene better. Above and in front of them hung a cloud of impenetrable darkness; below the rolling waves, distinguishable only by the phosphorescent gleams of their white crests, came in fierce succession, whilst the roar of wind gave sharp contradiction to the belief that the storm was abating. But along the range of vision —how near or extended that was it was impossible to say—no light was visible.

'There's a ship out somewhere—and in danger,' Nelly persisted. 'There's the gun again! Do you not hear it?'

They could not hear it. It was hard indeed to hear anything in the uproar outside. They strained their eyes and ears to see or hear some indication, but without success.

'The gun! I hear it now,' said Eph, after a long pause, as a sound came, palpable enough this time, to all ears.

'No, that's not a gun. That,' said the keeper, 'is a knocking at the door below. Who can it be? What can it be—in such a night, and in such a storm?'

There was an unmistakable thundering at the door! They listened with palpitating hearts. It could not be the rolling surge, for the door was at the side remote from the waves. It was possibly some wreck which had been cast on the stone stairs outside leading up to it, which had caught in the massive iron railings, and which the waves, in their retreat, were beating against. Whatever it was, it sounded ominously on their ears, as the knocking came dully, and with cavernous sound, up the stairs.

'Come down and let us see,' said the keeper at last. 'Who knows what it may be?'

Desiring Nelly to remain where she was in safety from the wind and storm, the keeper and his assistant descended; but Nelly, terrified at the idea of remaining alone in the darkness, went after them. Anything was better than remaining alone by herself, in the lightless gloom, with the storm-fiends shrieking outside. The knocking continued as they went down, growing louder as they drew near the under-storey. It was as if a giant's hand were hammering.

'What can it be?' asked Nelly in subdued terror. 'No living thing could be outside in such a storm as this.'

'Who knows?' said the keeper, with unshaken resolution, 'strange things happen in a storm. Help me to unfasten the door.'

With great difficulty they unbarred it, and withdrew the great bolt that closed it. It swung open. A great white sweep of wave and foam came rushing backwards, and in the doorway, in strong relief against its snowy surface, a man's form, shrouded and muffled, stood with hand extended upwards.

'Sam Hellings!' cried Nelly, in an agony of terror; but before they had time to speak or move further, the wave came rushing in, flooding the apartment, and extinguishing fire and light. It seemed also to bear the untoward visitor on its breast into the apartment. The ebbing wave, however, soon retreated, leaving the suddenly-darkened room as speedily empty as it was flooded; and the keeper, with rare presence of mind, threw himself against the opened door, closed it, and shot back the bar just as another wave came roaring inward over the rocks.

'Is he alive, Eph? Is he alive?' called out the keeper in great anxiety.

But Eph did not reply.

'Oh, father—a light, a light!' cried Nelly in fear, 'there's something in the room with us! I'll die if you leave me in darkness. There someone going upstairs. Oh, father!'

The keeper got the lights off the shelf, struck one, lit a lamp, and looked around. The floor was covered with miniature lakes, which the retreating wave had left behind, and with small articles of furniture which it had unceremoniously swept about. But, singularly enough, lying on it, too, as if the force of the wave had hurled him against the wall and stunned him, or the shock had been too much for his nerves, was the unconscious form of the assistant. But there was no other presence—there was no one, living or dead, but the three. The keeper looked around in amazement, then at the white face of his daughter.

'Nelly,' he asked, in a low tone, 'what is the meaning of this? Wasn't that Sam Hellings? Where is he?'

'I don't know, father. Sam Hellings was there, and came in with the sea. And—I don't think he could have gone out.'

Her father looked at her for a second in dazed bewilderment.

'I heard the door open, and someone go upstairs,' Nelly said, trembling.

'God bless us! Gone upstairs! I must go up and see. If anyone has gone up, Nelly, it's with no good intention. Sam Hellings, too! Providence be about us!'

Lighting a second lamp for her, and taking the one he held with him, the old man anxiously, but resolutely, proceeded upstairs. After some time he descended—what a long time it seemed to her, waiting below!

There was an unusual look of fear and affright on his face when he returned.

'Nelly,' he said, with bated breath, 'no one went upstairs—no living being anyhow, for there is no one there now, or on the way. But—the light was out —out, Nelly, blind out!'

'Oh, my!' cried Nelly remembering her brother and lover. 'Father, don't say that.'

'Either it went out with the storm or was put out, Nelly. But it was out for some time, for the lamp was cold.'

'Oh, father, father!' cried Nelly, wringing her hands, 'and that ship in distress—and Frank and Willie Strafford rounding the head. Oh, what will be done? Is it all right now?'

'It's all right now, Nelly. But, God help us! Who knows what harm may have been. How could it have happened? It was never so before, but—the night Oliver was drowned.'

Nelly shuddered remembering the dreadful coincidence — shuddered when she thought of her brother and lover on the dark, pitiless sea, with no friendly light to guide them—shuddered most of all when she thought of the conversation that had occurred in the earlier portion of the night between herself and the assistant. The unconscious form of the latter, however, needing their assistance, helped, in some degree, to distract their thoughts from the extinguishment of the lamps. It required a great deal of ministering to bring him to; and when he did recover consciousness, they were unable to ascertain from him whether it was fright or injury which caused his fit.

It was a long night—the longest either had ever known—but when the grey dawn came at last on the face of the troubled waters, they went upstairs to take note of what was passing outside. As far as the eye could reach, the sea was one mass of brown waves, capped and crested with foam. The wind had gone down, but the agitated sea came still tumultuously beating upon the rocks and throwing clouds of spray high against the lighthouse tower. Drifting upon the waves, now lifted in the air, now down in the trough, was timber—huge fragments of vessels which had foundered at sea during the night.

When the day still further advanced the sea abated. Rounding the head they could see, to their surprise, the coastguard boat coming towards them from the land. Connecting its advent with the extinguishment of the lamps during the night, the lighthouse keeper, with much perturbation of spirit, watched it enter the little land-locked cove, among the rocks, and proceeded to meet it.

'Father.'

It was not Nelly's voice that called to him this time, for, looking downwards, with a start, the keeper saw, to his extreme delight, the form of his son Frank standing below him, who presently was beside him, embracing him with every manifestation of rejoicing.

'The lifeboat was coming here,' said the young fellow, 'and I, anxious to see you, came with it. We reached port in the middle of the hurricane last night. But, oh father, we had an awfully narrow escape. We could not see the light with the storm, and could not see the channel or the buoys. We were within a heart's beat of being lost—if the ship had missed the middle passage we should have gone on the rocks and every soul would have been lost. A miracle could not have saved us. In the extremity of our danger we fired the signal gun—once, twice, thrice, and lo and behold! the lights flashed out—we knew where we were, and were saved. But it was a moment of awful danger, father. Our lives hung by a single thread. But we ran in all right under reefed sails, and —here I am!'

'I am perplexed, Frank. I think the place is bewitched. The lights were out last night.'

'Out!' repeated his son with an expression of horror. 'Out! And on such a night. Oh, don't say that, father.'

'Out they were, Frank. And—do you remember Sam Hellings?'

'Sam Hellings!' cried the young sailor, not a little wondering at this sudden digression, 'of course, I do. Why, he—'

'He came to the door last night in the height of the storm,' the keeper interrupted, with the same strange expression on his face his son had noted before. 'I don't know how he did, or could, but—he was there! And 'twas he warned me, Frank!—warned me in time to save your life.'

'Don't talk wildly like that, father,' cried Frank, in great pain and distress, for he though the old man had certainly grown demented. 'The thing is impossible. Sam Hellings sailed with us. We picked him up at Vera Cruz—but he met with an accident, and died two days ago, and we buried him at sea.'

'He came to the door last night,' the keeper reiterated in a solemn whisper, which was not without a tincture of fear in it. 'I saw him, and knew him, and so did Nelly—sure as you are standing there. He came in and went upstairs—wherever he went after.'

'Heaven help you, father, what are you talking about? I tell you Sam Hellings sailed with us. He fell from the rigging, poor fellow, and was badly hurt. Willie and I were kind to him, and minded him to the last. He was always talking of poor Oliver's death. But he died at last and was buried at sea two days ago—as we came near the Irish Sea.'

'Dead or alive, buried or unburied, he came to the door last night. And it was through him that the lamps were lit. He looked at me like—'

'Father, come away—come inside,' said his son with pained affection. 'I want to see Nelly. Look, they are hailing us from the boat. Willie Strafford—I forgot to tell you he is here—is calling to me. They are all hailing me. There must be something up. Come over to them.'

They were indeed, all beckoning to them, hailing them, gesticulating at them from the boat. A group of excited forms were gathered together there—around some object invisible to father and son. Going over, and way being made for them, the first glance showed them a figure lying in a cleft of the rocks; the second—

But what the second showed is best expressed by the exclamation of the lighthouse-keeper:

'Gracious heavens! Frank, see!—Sam Hellings!'

Sam Hellings, indeed, it was. Wrapped up in the coarse canvas shrouding, through which head and extended arm alone protruded—the iron weight which had failed to sink him still attached to his feet—he lay in mute and solemn stillness.

'It was that weight—I see it all now,' said the lighthouse-keeper somewhat incoherently, after a long pause of breathless silence, during which they gazed at the stirless form before them. 'It was that weight that caught in the iron rails outside, and that caused the knocking at the door. The uplifted arm too! How could he come here, Frank! Buried two days ago at sea!'

'He came in with the beating storm—came to save my life in return for Oliver's,' said Frank, in a low voice, as he stooped down and reverently drew the tangled seaweed from the dead man's face. He was always sorrowing during his illness aboard ship for being the unfortunate cause of poor Oliver's death. He came now to save mine instead.'

'I've seen many strange things at sea during my time,' said the old man, 'but this is the strangest of all. Who could have thought he'd be about the light-house, of all places in the world, last night. It was his face that Nelly saw looking in through the window-pane out of the storm, after all. And it was his voice that cried to me in my sleep.'

'He knew the lamps were out, and wanted to waken you and warn you,' said his son.

But whatever further he had to say was interrupted; for Nelly had come unexpectedly behind the group whilst they were thus debating and flung two white welcoming arms in joy around her brother's neck, thus effectually precluding all further discussion.

Eph, the assistant, during the course of the day disappeared.

One night, many years after when the lighthouse-keeper had long lain in Kilbarrack churchyard, in the shadow of Howth Head, and Willie Strafford and Nelly Williams kept the place he occupied, and the events of the night had fallen into the dim region of tradition, a hurricane, not unlike that recorded, swept over the coasts and the Irish Sea. As before, it made the lighthouse the target of its fury, and when morning came the shore and the rocks surrounding were strewn with wreck; for many vessels had not been as fortunate as *The Dalkey Pride* on the previous occasion, or had not been steered by skilful hands, and ships had gone on the unpitying rocks, and had been shivered to pieces as if they had been built of matchwood.

Searchers went down over the rocks to see if any good could be effected or lives saved when the gale abated. The story of the Warning was brought once more vividly to their minds; for, in the same cleft of the rocks where the body of Sam Hellings had been found—covered like his, too, with masses of netting seaweed—the dead body of the former assistnt lighthouse-keeper lay! The vessel in which he was sailing must have been coming homewards—having, indeed, entered the bay—must have gone on Howth Head in the gale, and been beaten to pieces by the raging waters, for rock and strand and beach were crowded with debris.

The searchers were not likely to have read Shakespeare, else they might have said: 'There are stranger things in Heaven and on earth, Horatio, than are dreamt of in our philosophy.'

This story is by James Murphy

5. Strange Things in the Sky

Few people would connect ghosts with aeroplanes, yet there are some startling stories in this sphere. The great airship *R101,* built by the British Air Minister Lord Thomson of Cardington, took off from England on a flight to India on 4 October 1930.

Seven hours later a radio message was heard: 'Fifteen miles south-west of Abbeville at fifteen hundred feet, speed thirty-eight miles-per-hour. After an excellent supper distinguished passengers have smoked final cigar and gone to bed.' This was the last message from the airship. At two o'clock in the morning it sank slowly to the ground at Beauvais, and burst into flames.

Lord Thomson was among the fifty-four dead; only six survived. Two days afterwards the famous ghost hunter, Harry Price, was having a seance with the medium, Mrs Eileen Garrett, when a masculine voice came through, saying he was Carmichael Irwin, captain of the *R101.* In a long technical discourse the voice said that the ship became unwieldy because she was waterlogged and buffeted by winds and her engines could not sustain her. She was 'too heavy by several tons'.

Strangely enough this was also stated by Major G. H. Scott, who had flown the smaller *R100,* after he inspected the *R101.* He decided however to go on the fatal trip and was among those who lost their lives.

On 22 October 1967 Captain Aidan Quigley was taking a flight out from Chicago to Dublin with

Captain Bartley O'Connor. When the meal was being served the senior hostess came into the cockpit and announced they were two dinners short; there were two passengers in row four whom she hadn't remembered seeing as they came on board, and they weren't on the seating list. There were dinners for 120, but there were 122 passengers. However, the crew did with less and so the extra pair got their meal.

Afterwards Captain Quigley left the cockpit and walked down to talk to the couple, described as 'strange' by the hostess. The man said his name was Vaalkar and introduced his wife, apologising 'for joining the flight at a late stage.' They both spoke with pronounced foreign accents. The conversation ranged about politics and world affairs. Then he asked unusual questions: 'Of what metal is this vessel composed? Why relate your speed to that of sound? Are you limited to this method of space travel? Are you confined to jet thrust for propulsive force?'

At this stage the wife cut in saying, 'Sergi you must not question so,' and taking the cue Captain Quigley excused himself and returned to the cockpit.

He appeared to be in a daze as Captain O'Connor looked at him on his return. 'Have a peep at that couple in row four and I'll take over,' he said. There was static interference on the radio and the radar screen was behaving strangely. Bartley O'Connor returned.

'Well?' Captain Quigley asked.

'I don't quite know what to think. Did you notice their skin?'

'Not particularly. The lights in that area are low.'

'It has the most unusual texture,' he said. 'They

both have the smoothest, whitest skin; no pores, no blemishes, no creases.'

'So,' Captain Quigley replied, 'they might have been Egyptians or high-cast Indians.'

'That's possible,' Bartley answered, 'but did you study their clothes? The tailoring was perfect. It was a strange material and cut angularly; no curves at all, even on the woman. The whole set up reminded me of a tailor's dummy.' He said the woman asked the most peculiar questions, and appeared 'to be a person of unusual intelligence.'

They flew on through the night admiring the wonderful lights of the Aurora Borealis. At dawn the passengers slumbered including the couple in row four. Later they asked the senior hostess how are our friends in row four. 'They're not there; they are probably in the washrooms,' she replied.

But they were not in the washrooms, nor indeed in the aeroplane. The Northern Lights were gone and with them the sweeping searchlights and the strangeness which Bartley had seen in the night sky. They went back separately to where the couple had been sitting. There was an extraordinary exotic odour about their seats, and the whole linen headrests were now flecked with a fine deposit of graphite.

'They'll never believe us,' said Captain O'Connor. They never did.

Captain Quigley dismissed the whole business from his mind, but later recalled it vividly when the Russians released a new bulletin on their cosmonaut Valkaar, whom they had been unable to recover from a polar orbit.

From **A Place in the Sky** *by Captain Aidan Quigley*

6. A Strange Light

'At my house on the shore of Clew Bay in County Mayo on 24 October 1962, at precisely a quarter past one in the morning my wife and I experienced an inexplicable situation. The circumstances were these:

'In addition to ourselves there were, visiting in the house, seven guests from America. We had, variously, been shooting, deep-sea fishing, and seeing certain points of interest in Mayo on that day. After cocktails we dined at nine o'clock, and then played bridge, talked, and went to bed. My wife went to our bedroom, directly above the drawing room, about midnight. All others followed to bed shortly afterwards, and I did the same within a few minutes, having turned out the lights on the ground floor.

'When I entered our darkened room and had closed the door, my wife stirred immediately from her sleep and asked uneasily if I saw the strange small ball of light in the air above our beds. She said that she was certain that it was a reflection of some sort, but had been unable to discover the source.

'I looked up and saw hovering, almost directly above my bed, a ball of light with the intensity of a radium-dial watch. I chose to tell my wife that the only thing I saw was a reflection and no light. She was relieved, and went back to sleep — as I pondered the incandescent ball, and undressed in the dark.

'I checked the draw-curtains and peered out of the windows into a moonless, pitchblack night. There were no cars or bicycles with headlights, no lighthouse beams, no stars, no lights that could have pierced the drawn and lined curtains; there was no fire in the grate. The sphere of light, about the size of a grapefruit and completely round, was there. It quivered while stationary, and seemed to drift a few inches each way.

'There was no atmosphere of malevolence about the circumstances, only one of uneasiness. With a thumping heart, I stood on top of my bed and put my hand gingerly through the ball of light. There was no feeling of heat or substance. My hand passed through it as if it were a shadow. I noted that even the slight current of air made by my hand did not budge it — as it might have a ring of smoke or fog.

'As I went to bed, and eventually to sleep, the ball shone dimly above the bed, quivered, and moved a bit vertically and horizontally. In the morning it was gone.

'My wife and I talked of the matter several times together after the occurrence, but never mentioned it to our house guests nor to anyone. Several things were quite certain: there had been no discussion of ghosts, legends, or other obviously provocative subjects prior to the fact of the ball of light; there was no light source — from within or without the bedroom — that could have caused the phenomenon; and, to our knowledge, there was no alleged precedent for such a thing.

'In August of the following year at dinner with us in the same house, a neighbour and dear friend, who knew nothing of our experience, asked if we had encountered a Dutch couple who had leased a house very near to us for the summer. We had not met them, but our friend, typically hospitable and kindly, had called upon them. The young Dutch wife told our neighbour of the pleasure that she, her husband, and two small children had been having in Ireland — but she commented on an extraordinary experience: she said that a strange glowing sphere appeared in their bedroom one night; she too pulled curtains, checked for reflections, and was, in the end, similarly perplexed and unnerved by the eerie ball of light.'

This was sent to my **Evening Herald** *ghost column by Mr Walter Curley when he was the American ambassador to Ireland.*

7. Franklin Delano Roosevelt from beyond the Grave

'Wish I could give one more fireside chat to tell the American people the greatest humbug of all is death. . .'

These electrifying words are just part of a stunning message that Franklin Delano Roosevelt sent back from beyond the grave, according to his longtime friend, former United States Minister to Ireland David Gray, who believed he contacted the spirit of the dead president through a top medium.

Gray, who was Minister to Ireland from 1940 to 1947, said in letters before his death that he had already obtained spirit writings in private sessions with the noted psychic Geraldine Cummins for some time before Franklin Delano Roosevelt's death in 1945. Gray said he was particularly interested in messages from a spirit who claimed to be Marguerite LeHand, Roosevelt's former private secretary, who died in 1944. The messages from LeHand came shortly before his death and continued until 1947.

On 25 March 1945, Miss Cummins' spirit writing spelled out: 'She [Miss LeHand] said Frank Roosevelt is coming over here in April.' Miss Cummins promptly wrote to Gray in Dublin and told him about her strange experience. Gray recalled in his letters that he was puzzled over that message, thinking that it meant that the president was going to make a trip from the United States to London.

On 12 April Roosevelt was dead, and for Gray the

message was clear.

It was in June 1945 — about two months after Franklin Delano Roosevelt's death — when, according to Cummins in her book *Mind in Life and Death,* Gray, the psychic, and her assistant sat down together at the United States legation in Dublin and awaited word from the departed president.

It came swiftly as in a trance, Miss Cummins wrote:

'David, you are a dear fellow to call me up and a scoundrel to have kept me waiting for this moment for weeks. Wish I could give one more fireside chat to tell the American people that the greatest humbug of all is death.

'I will remember that last warm morning. I think it was horror at the prospect of a detestable lunch of gruel that made me collapse. I had that terrible pain for only a few moments, then darkness–delicious, like black velvet, and afterwards, no pain, just waking up like a child.

'I was very active at my funeral, and the only one who paid any attention to me at that funeral was Scottie my dog. I was very amused at all the best brains in the country concentrating on that shabby old garment of mine that was being put under the earth, and there was I, as large as life, and when my dog saw me, he rolled on the ground — making quite a bit of diversion. But nobody guessed he rolled on the grass with joy because he saw me.

'I went into a body like my own body, young, healthy, strong, and no one at my funeral saw me, because this body was travelling a little faster than theirs.

'We are going off on a wonderful cruise on the

broad seas of eternity. And I am going to have the finest holiday of my life.'

Gray himself died in 1968. Geraldine Cummins passed away in 1969.

A spokesman for the American Society for Psychic Research said: 'Geraldine Cummins is considered one of the founding grandmothers of the psychic movement. She was well regarded in the psychic community.'

8. A Haunted House

'I was ordered by my physician, my health being in an unsatisfactory state, to change my residence to one upon the sea-coast; and accordingly, I took a house for a year in a fashionable watering-place, at a moderate distance from the city in which I had previously resided, and connected with it by a railway.

'Winter was setting in when my move was decided upon; but there was nothing whatever dismal or depressing in the change. The house I had taken was quite a modern one. It stood in a cheerful row, with small gardens in front, facing the sea, and commanding sea air and sea views in perfection. In the rear it had coach-house and stable, and between them and the house a considerable grass-plot with some flower beds.

'Our family consisted of my wife and myself, with three children, the eldest about nine years old, she and the next in age being girls; and the youngest, between six and seven, a boy. To these were added six servants, whom, although for certain reasons I decline giving their real names, I shall indicate, for the sake of clearness, by arbitrary ones. There was a nurse, Mrs Southerland; a nursery-maid, Ellen Page; the cook, Mrs Greenwood; and the housemaid, Ellen Faith; a butler, whom I shall call Smith, and his son, James.

'We came out to take possession at about seven o'clock in the evening; everything was comfortable and cheery; good fires lighted, the rooms neat and airy, and a general air of preparation and comfort, highly conducive to good spirits and pleasant anticipation.

'The sitting-rooms were large and cheerful and they and the bedrooms more than ordinarily lofty, the kitchen and servants' rooms, on the same level, were well and comfortably furnished, and had, like the rest of the house, an air of recent painting and fitting up, and a completely modern character, which imparted a very cheerful air of cleanliness and convenience.

'There had been just enough of the fuss of settling agreeably to occupy us, and to give a pleasant turn to our thoughts after we had retired to our rooms. Being an invalid, I had a small bed to myself—resigning the four-poster to my wife. The candle was extinguished, but a night-light was burning. I was coming upstairs, and she, already in bed, had just dismissed her maid, when we were both startled by a wild scream from her room; I found her in a state of extreme agitation and terror. She insisted that she had seen an unnaturally tall figure come beside her in bed and stand there. The light was too faint to enable her to define anything of this apparition, but she had distinctly seen such a colourless shape.

'We both endeavoured to reassure her. The room once more looked so cheerful in the candlelight, that we were quite uninfluenced by her terrors. The movements and voices of the servants downstairs still getting things into their places and completing our comfortable arrangements, had also their effect in steeling us against any such influence, and we set the whole thing down as a dream, or an imperfectly-seen outline of the bed-curtains. When, however, we were alone, my wife reiterated, still in great agitation, her clear assertion that she had most positively seen, being at the time as completely awake as ever she was, precisely what she had described to us. And in this conviction she continued perfectly firm.

'A day or two after this, it came out that our servants were under an apprehension that, somehow or other, thieves had established a secret mode of access to the lower part of the house. The butler, Smith, had seen an ill-looking woman in his room on the first night of our arrival; and he and other servants constantly saw, for many days subsequently, glimpses of a retreating figure, which corresponded with that so seen by him, passing through a passage which led to a back area in which were some coal vaults.

'This figure was seen always in the act of retreating, its back turned, generally getting round the corner of the passage into the area, in a stealthy and hurried way, and, when closely followed, imperfectly seen again entering one of the coal vaults, and when pursued into it, nowhere to be found.

'The idea of anything supernatural had, strange to say, not yet entered the mind of anyone of the servants. They had heard some stories of smugglers having secret passages into houses, and using their means of access for purposes of pillage, or with a view to frightening superstitious people out of houses which they needed for their own objects, and a suspicion of similar practices here, caused them extreme uneasiness. The apparent anxiety also manifested by this retreating figure to escape observation, and always appearing to leave at the same point, favoured this romantic hypothesis. The men, however, made a most careful examination of the back area, and of the coal vaults, with a view to discover some means of exit, but entirely without success.

'I called the man, Smith, to hear from his own lips the particulars of what he had seen; and certainly his report was very curious. I give it as literally as my memory enables me. His son slept in the same room, and was sound asleep; but he lay awake, as men sometimes will on a change of bed, and having many things on his mind. He was lying with his face towards the wall, but observing a light and some little stir in the room, he turned round in his bed, and saw the figure of a woman, squalid, and ragged in dress; her figure rather low and broad. She had some-thing—either a cloak or shawl—on, and wore a bonnet. Her back was turned, and she appeared to be searching or rummaging for something on the floor, and, without appearing to observe him, she turned towards him. The light, which was more like the intense glow of a coal, as he described it, being of a deep red colour, proceeded from the hollow of her hand, which she held beside her head, and he saw her perfectly distinctly. She appeared middle-aged, was deeply pitted with the smallpox, and blind in one eye. His phrase in describing her general appearance was, that she was "a miserable, poor-looking creature."

'He was under the impression that she must be the woman who had been left by the proprietor in charge of the house, and who that evening, having given up the keys, remained for some little time with the female servants. He coughed, therefore, to make her aware of his presence, and turned towards the wall. When he again looked round she and the light were gone; and odd as was her method of lighting herself in her search, the circumstances excited neither uneasiness nor curiosity in his mind, until he discovered next morning that the woman in question had left the house long before he had gone to his bed.

'I examined the man very closely as to the appearance of the person who had visited him, and the result was what I have described. It struck me as an odd thing, that even then, considering how prone to superstition persons in his rank of life usually are, he did not seem to suspect anything supernatural in the occurrence; and, on the countrary, was thoroughly persuaded that his visitor was a living person, who had got into the house by some hidden entrance.

'On Sunday, on his return from his place of worship, he told me that, when the service was ended, and the congregation was making their way slowly out, he saw the very woman in the crowd. He kept his eye upon her for several minutes, but such was the crush, that all his efforts to reach her were unavailing, and when he got into the open street she was gone. He was quite positive as to his having distinctly seen her for several minutes, and fully impressed with the substantial and living reality of his visitor, he was very much provoked at her having escaped him. He made inquiries also in the neighbourhood, but could procure no information, nor hear of any other persons having seen any woman corresponding with his visitor.

'The cook and the housemaid occupied a bedroom on the kitchen floor. It had whitewashed walls, and they were actually terrified by the appearance of the shadow of a woman passing and repassing across the side wall opposite to their beds. They suspected that this had been going on much longer than they were aware, for its presence was discovered by a sort of accident.

'This shadow always moved upon one particular wall, returning after short intervals, and causing them extreme terror. They placed the candle, as the most obvious specific, so close to the infested wall, that the flame all but touched it; and believed for some time that they had effectually got rid of this annoyance. But one night, notwithstanding this arrangement of the light, the shadow returned, passing and repassing, as before, upon the same wall, although their only candle was burning within an inch of it. It was obvious that no substance capable of casting such a shadow could have interposed; and, indeed, as they described it, the shadow seemed to have no sort of relation to the position of the light, and appeared in manifest defiance of the laws of optics.

'I ought to mention that the housemaid was a particularly fearless sort of person, as well as a very honest one. Her companion, the cook was a scrupulously religious woman, and both agreed in every particular in their relation of what occurred.

'Meanwhile, the nursery was not without its annoyances, though as yet of a comparatively trivial kind. Sometimes, at night, the handle of the door was turned hurriedly as if by a person trying to come in, and at others a knocking was made at it. These sounds occurred after the children had settled to sleep, and while the nurse still remained awake.

Whenever she called to know "who is there?" the sounds ceased; but several times, and particularly at first, she was under the impression that they were caused by her mistress, who had come to see the children. Thus impressed she had got up and opened the door, expecting to see her, but discovering only darkness, and receiving no answer to her inquiries.

'One morning, I think about three or four weeks after our arrival, I was sitting at the parlour window which looked to the front, when I saw the little iron door to the garden pushed open by a woman who so exactly answered the description given by Smith of the woman who had visited his room that I was instantly impressed that she must be the same person. She was a square, short woman, dressed in soiled and tattered clothes, scarred and pitted with smallpox, and blind in one eye. She stepped hurriedly into the little enclosure, and peered from a distance of a few yards into the room where I was sitting. I felt that now was the moment to clear the matter up; but there was something stealthy in the manner and look of the woman which convinced me that I must not appear to notice her until her retreat was fairly cut off. Unfortunately, I was suffering from a lame foot, and could not reach the bell as quickly as I wished. I made all the haste I could, and rang violently to bring up the servant Smith. In the short interval that intervened, I observed the woman from the window, who having in a leisurely way, and with a kind of scrutiny, looked along the front windows of the house, passed quickly out again, closing the gate after her, and followed a lady who was walking along the footpath at a quick pace, as if with the intention of begging from her.

The moment the man entered I told him—"the blind woman you described to me has this instant followed a lady in that direction. Try to overtake her." He was, if possible, more eager than I in the chase, but returned in a short time after a vain pursuit, very hot, and utterly disappointed. And, thereafter, we saw her face no more.

'All this time, and up to the period of our leaving the house, which was not for two or three months later, there occurred at intervals the only phenomenon in the entire series having any resemblance to what we hear described as "spiritualism". This was a knocking, like a soft hammering with a wooden mallet, as it seemed in the timbers between the bedroom ceilings and the roof. It had special peculiarity, that it was always rhythmical, and invariably the emphasis was upon the last stroke. It would sound rapidly one, two, three, *four*—one, two, three, *four;* or one, two, *three*—one, two, *three,* and sometimes one, *two*—one, *two,* etc., and this, with intervals and resumptions, monotonously for hours at a time.

'At first this caused my wife, who was a good deal confined to her bed, much annoyance; and we sent to our neighbours to inquire if any hammering or carpentering was going on in their houses, but were informed that nothing of the sort was taking place. I have myself heard it frequently, always in the same inaccessible part of the house, and with the same monotonous emphasis. One odd thing about it was, that on my wife's calling out, as she used to do when it became more than usually troublesome, "stop that noise," it was invariably arrested for a longer or shorter time.

'Of course none of these occurrences were ever mentioned in the children's hearing. They would have been, no doubt, like most children, greatly terrified had they heard anything of the matter, and known that their elders were unable to account for what was passing. Their fears would have made them wretched and troublesome.

'They used to play for some hours every day in the back garden—the house forming one end of this oblong enclosure, the stable and coach-house the other, and two parallel walls of considerable height the sides. Here, as it afforded a perfectly safe playground, they were frequently left quite to themselves; and in talking over their days' adventures, as children will, they happened to mention a woman, or rather the woman, for they had long grown familiar with her appearance, whom they used to see in the garden while they were at play. They assumed that she came in and went out at the stable door, but they never actually saw her enter or depart. They merely saw a figure—that of a very poor woman, soiled and ragged—near the stable wall, stooping over the ground, and apparently grubbing in the loose clay in search of something. She did not disturb, or appear to observe them; and they left her in undisturbed possession of her nook of ground. When seen it was always in the same spot, and similarly occupied; and the description they gave of her general appearance—for they never saw her face—corresponded with that of the one-eyed woman whom Smith, and subsequently as it seemed, I, had seen.

'The other man, James, who looked after a mare which I had purchased for the purpose of riding exercise, had, like everyone else in the house, his little trouble to report, though it was not much. The stall in which, as the most comfortable, it was decided to place the mare, she peremptorily declined to enter. Though a very docile and gentle little animal, there was no getting her into it. She would snort and rear, and, in fact, do or suffer anything rather than set her hoof in it. He was obliged, therefore, to place her in another. And on several occasions he found her there, exhibiting all the equine symptoms of extreme fear. Like the rest of us, however, this man was not troubled in the particular case with any super-stitious qualms. The mare had evidently been fright-ened; and he was puzzled to find out how, or by whom, for the stable was well secured, and had, I am nearly certain, a lock-up yard outside.

'One morning I was greeted with the news that robbers had certainly got into the house in the night; and that one of them had actually been seen in the nursery. The witness, I found, was my eldest child, then about nine years of age. Having awoken in the night, and lain awake for some time in her bed, she heard the handle of the door turn, and a person whom she distinctly saw—for it was a light night, and the window-shutters unclosed—but whom she had never seen before, stepped in cautiously on tiptoe. He was a rather small man, with a very red face; he wore an oddly cut frock coat, the collar of which stood up, and trousers, rough and wide, like those of a sailor, turned up at the ankles, and either short boots or clumsy shoes, covered with mud. This man listened beside the nurse's bed, which stood next to the door, as if to satisfy himself that she was sleeping soundly; and having done so for some seconds, he began to move cautiously in a diagonal line, across the room to the chimney-piece, where he stood for a while, and so resumed his tiptoe walk, skirting the wall, until he reached a chest of drawers, some of which were open, and into which he looked, and began to rummage in a hurried way, supposedly searching for something worth taking away. He then passed on to the window, where there was a dressing-table, at which he also stopped, turning over the things upon it, and standing for some time at the window as if looking out. Then resuming his walk by the side wall opposite he returned in the same way towards the foot of the nurse's bed. My eldest child watched these proceedings in extreme terror. As he drew near she instinctively moved herself in the bed, with her head and shoulders to the wall, drawing up her feet; but he passed by without appearing to observe, or, at least, to care for her presence. Immediately after the nurse turned in her bed as if about to waken; and when the child, who had drawn the clothes about her head, again ventured to peep out, the man was gone.

'The child had no idea of her having seen anything more formidable than a thief. On hearing her perfectly distinct and consistent account I could myself arrive at no other conclusion than that a stranger had actually got into the house. I had, therefore, in the first instance, a most careful examination made to discover any traces of an entrance having been made by any window into the house. The doors had been found barred and locked as usual; but no sign of anything of the sort was discernible. I then had the various articles—plate, wearing apparel, books, etc., counted; and having looked over and reckoned up everything, it became quite clear that nothing whatever had been removed from the house, nor was there the slightest indication of anything having been so much as disturbed there. I must state here that this child was remarkably clear, intelligent, and observant; and that her description of the man and of all that had occurred was most exact, and as detailed as the want of light rendered possible.

'I felt assured that an entrance had actually been effected into the house, though for what purpose was not easily to be conjectured. Smith was equally confident on this point; and his theory was that the object was simply to frighten us out of the house by making us believe it haunted; and he was more than ever anxious and on the alert to discover the conspirators. It often since appeared odd to me. Every year, indeed, more odd, as this cumulative case of the marvellous becomes more and more inexplicable to my mind. Underlying my sense of mystery was all along the quiet assumption that all these occurrences were one way or another referable to natural causes. I could not account for them, indeed, myself; but during the whole period I inhabited that house, I never once felt, though much alone, and often up very late at night, any of those tremors and thrills which everyone has at times experienced when situation and the hour are favourable. Except the cook and housemaid, who were plagued with the shadow I mentioned crossing and recrossing upon the bedroom wall, we all, without exception, experienced the same strange sense of security, and regarded these phenomena rather with a perplexed sort of interest and curiosity, than with any more unpleasant sensations.

'The knockings which I have mentioned at the nursery door, preceded generally by the sound of a step on the lobby, meanwhile continued. At that time (for my wife, like myself, was an invalid) two eminent physicians, who came out occasionally by rail, were attending us. These gentlemen were at first only amused, but ultimately interested, and very much puzzled by the occurrences which we described. One of them, at last, recommended that a candle should be kept burning upon the lobby. It was in fact a recurrence to an old woman's recipe against ghosts—of course it might be serviceable, too, against impostors. We fancied that it was successful; for there was an interval of quiet for, I think, three or four nights. But after that, the noises—the footsteps on the lobby —the knocking at the door, and the turning of the handle recommenced in full force, notwithstanding the light upon the table outside; and these particular phenomena became only more perplexing than ever.

'The alarm of robbers and smugglers gradually subsided afer a week or two; but we were again to hear news from the nursery. Our second little girl, then between seven and eight years of age, saw in the night time — she alone being awake — a young woman, with black, or very dark hair, which hung loose, and with a black cloak on, standing near the middle of the floor, opposite the hearth-stone, and fronting the foot of her bed. She appeared quite unobservant of the children and nurse sleeping in the room. She was very pale, and looked, the child said, both "sorry and frightened", and with something very peculiar and terrible about her eyes, which made the child think that she was dead. She was looking, not at, but in the direction of the child's bed, and there was a dark streak across her throat, like a scar with blood upon it. This figure was not motionless; but once or twice turned slowly, and without appearing to be conscious of the presence of the child, or the other occupants of the room, like a person in a trance. There was on this occasion a night-light burning in the room; and the child saw, or thought she saw, all these details with perfect distinctness. She got her head under the bed-clothes; and although a good many years have passed since then, she cannot recall the spectacle without feelings of peculiar horror.

'One day, when the children were playing in the back garden, I asked them to point out to me the spot where they were accustomed to seeing the woman near the stable wall. There was no division of opinion as to this precise point, which they indicated in the most confident way. I suggested that, perhaps, something might be hidden there in the ground; and advised them to dig a hole there with their little spades. Accordingly, to work they went, and by my return in the evening they had dug up a piece of jaw-bone, with several teeth in it. The bone was very much decayed, and ready to crumble to pieces, but the teeth were quite sound. I could not tell whether they were human grinders; but I showed the fossil to one of the physicians I have mentioned, who came out the next evening, and he pronounced them human teeth. The same conclusion was arrived at a day or two later by the other medical man. It appears to me now, on reviewing the whole matter, almost unaccountable that, with such evidence before me, I should not have got in a labourer, and had the spot effectually dug and searched. I can only say, that so it was. I was quite satisfied of the moral truth of every word that-had been related to me, and which I have here set down with scrupulous accuracy. But I experienced an apathy, for which neither then nor afterwards did I quite know how to account for. I had a vague, but immovable impression that the whole affair was referable to natural agencies. It was not until some time after we had left the house, which, by-the-by, we afterwards found had had the reputation of being haunted, that on reconsideration I found it difficult to account satisfactorily for all that had occurred. A great deal we might arbitrarily set down to imagination. But even in so doing there was the oddity, not to say improbability, of so many different persons having nearly simultaneously suffered from different spectral and other illusions during the short period for which we had occupied that house, who never before, nor so far as we learned, afterwards were troubled by any fears or fancies of the sort. There were other things, too, not to be so accounted for. The odd knockings in the roof I frequently heard myself.

'There were also in the day-time, rappings at the doors of the sitting-rooms, which constantly deceived us. Our "Come ins" went unanswered, and the hall or passage outside the door was discovered to be empty.

'About a week after the discovery of the teeth, which were found, I think, about two feet under the ground, a friend, much advanced in years, who remembered the town, happened to pay us a visit. He good-humouredly pooh-poohed the whole thing; but at the same time was evidently curious about it. "We might construct a sort of story," said I, "and assign to each of the three figures who appeared their respective parts in some dreadful tragedy enacted in this house. The male figure represents the murderer; the ill-looking one-eyed woman his accomplice, who, we will suppose, buried the body where she is now so often seen grubbing in the earth, and where the human teeth and jaw-bone have so lately been disinterred; the young woman with dishevelled tresses, and black cloak, and the bloody scar across her throat, their victim. A difficulty, however, which I cannot get over, exists in the cheerfulness, the great publicity, and the evident very recent date of the house."

"'Why, as to that," said he, "the house is *not* modern; it and those beside it formed an old government store, altered and fitted up recently as you see. I remember it well in my young days, fifty years ago, before the town had grown out in this direction, and a more entirely lonely spot, or one more fitted for the commission of a secret crime, could not have been imagined."

'I have nothing to add, for very soon after this my physician pronounced a longer stay unnecessary for my health, and we took our departure. I may add, that although I have lived for considerable periods in many other houses, I never experienced any annoyances of a similar kind elsewhere; neither have I made (stupid dog! you will say), any inquiries respecting either the antecedents or subsequent history of the house in which we made so disturbed a sojourn. I was content with what I knew, and have here related as clearly as I could, and I think it a very pretty puzzle as it stands.'

This story by Sheridan Le Fanu first appeared in the Dublin University Magazine in 1862.

9.   A Memory of My Own

When I was very young I lived next door to an old man who was approaching his ninetieth year. He had been reared by an aunt in Thomas Street, Dublin, who had looked out of her window to see the execution of Robert Emmet in the street in 1803! But to me, what was more interesting was the old man's amazing repertoire of ghost stories about old Dublin.

There was one about a house in Marrowbone Lane where people were lifted up in the air as they climbed the stairs, and another about one of the residences of the Guinness family where barrels were seen moving around for no apparent reason. And there was the ghost of a character known as 'Larry the Wax' (a cobbler, no doubt) who appeared on and off around the Meath Street area to frighten innocent passers-by.

Best of all, however, was his story about the 'Devil on the Rialto', not Shakespeare's Venice, but the old Rialto Bridge in Dublin. The period was the 1890s. Here is the story as he told it to me one dark November evening, as the wind howled outside.

'We were working as lamp-lighters at the time, that is Mick Sallenger and meself, and between us we lit all the old gas lamps between Dolphin's Barn and Inchicore. We had the habit of meeting at different spots during our labours.

'On this particular, dark, dismal, December evening we agreed to meet halfway through our beat in Larry Byrne's pub near Rialto Bridge. My friend was there when I arrived, and after a few half ones we were ready for the second part of our labours. Mick decided he would light the odd few lamps between Rialto Bridge and the First Lock. We agreed to have "one for the road" in Larry's when our labours were completed.

'We parted outside, and I went on to light my section which was down towards James's Street Harbour. Over half an hour later I returned to Larry Byrne's. My friend, Mick, had not arrived, so I ordered a whiskey and sat down to await him.

'I was in the middle of a chat with the barman, when there was a shattering sound, and to our amazement we turned around to see my friend Mick come crashing through the door. He stumbled onto a seat and I quickly got him a whiskey. It was a while before I got a word out of him.

'"What happened?" I asked. He muttered something like "the dog, the dog". It was some time before we got the story. Apparently Mick was coming back the dark lonely walk from the first lock alongside the canal when to his horror he saw the figure of a large hound coming towards him. Its eyes were blazing and it looked as if its paws were about to tear his throat out. "It was the Devil," he said. He ran for his life, and as he did so the dog sprang into the air, over Mick's head, and splashed into the canal almost under Rialto Bridge.

'Mick remembered little after that until he found himself being plied with whiskey in Larry Byrne's pub. Needless to remark we did this particular patrol together after that, and got out of that area as fast as we could.'

On the wall outside the gate of the former Grand Canal Company's headquarters at James's Street Harbour a stone head of a much weathered face with large ears may be seen. It had once been underneath the eighteenth century Rialto Bridge. It was placed in its present position when the old bridge was demolished in the 1930s, and is said by local people to represent the devil.

10. The Ghosts of Rathgar

The most terrifying ghost story I know is Henry James's *Turn of the Screw* and I think that is because it concerns the haunting of children—by daylight as well as dark. None of the ghosts with whom I am, so to speak, acquainted, are fond of daylight; but there is, a few streets away from where I live, a haunted garden.

I am convinced that some time in the future our neighbourhood will be full of dispossessed garden ghosts because those long walled back gardens are vanishing with such rapidity under a blizzard of dust as the bulldozers batter their way through old brick walls and apple trees, pergolas and rose bowers, to make way for apartment blocks of quite amazing ugliness. But so far the haunted garden in the vicinity of Kenilworth Square has not fallen to the despoilers. It is still there behind its sheltering walls, overgrown and neglected, full of healthy weeds—except sometimes on hot Saturday afternoons in summer!

The story was told to me by a reliable authority and it goes like this. A student rented a top room in the house next door. He was exhausted having moved in with his possessions and settled them into some sort of order, so he decided to forget about the blazing sun outside and take a few hours rest. But before he did he leaned against his open window and looked regretfully down at the cheerful scene in the next-door garden. The end of that garden had been turned into a tennis court and a game of mixed doubles was in progress. It was the time of year when student frolics take place all over the city, and this lot were dressed up in graceful outdated tennis gear, but they played a fast game all the same. The spectators sat around in floppy hats and boaters, and the young girls carrying refreshment trays wore long frilled aprons and caps with floating ribbons. The laughter and the whang of the tennis balls came up to him from the garden as he finally dropped asleep on his bed.

He did not wake up until after dark, so there was nothing of the next-door garden to be seen, nor any voices to be heard. Next morning he couldn't believe what he saw—last year's leaves were rotting along the overgrown walks, brambles everywhere; and down at the bottom of the garden the remains of two posts on which a tennis net had once hung. Local residents, he learned, were quite familiar with the ghostly tennis parties.

Once in the summer of 1959 we looked at several nearby houses up for sale, and they all had that odd feeling of cold on a warm day which tells the cowardly to look elsewhere for a home. At that time the most haunted house in the whole district was still standing gaunt at the corner of the square empty, by then, for twenty years or more. People sent to look at it by the auctioneers always found it occupied—a face at an upper window, a man and a woman in evening dress on the first landing, footsteps down in the kitchen, a clatter of heels on the bare staircase when nobody was there. The auctioneers gave up trying to sell it and tried renting it, but nobody ever stayed there longer than a couple of weeks. It was the scene, some say, of a double murder in the last century. It was finally bought by a firm of car dealers and demolished to make way for extensive showrooms, a filling station, and shops. If those premises are haunted today it is by hopefuls in search of a bargain.

I mentioned the warning cold which tells the cowardly to seek elsewhere for a home but when we first stepped into our house it was warm and friendly-seeming. Yet it houses 'Horatio' as well as ourselves and has done so for more than twenty years. He is, I like to think, as tolerant of us as we are of him, and you never actually see him. You can never precisely predict when you will hear 'Horatio' either, but it is always at night and usually in the winter. He comes with a heavy man's stride up the front steps and you hear him putting his key in the lock. You hear the hall door opening and his footsteps along the upper hall. They always stop outside the same room which used to be a bedroom, his, I think, and is now a bathroom.

During the first winter we spent here I was fooled by him time and again. I would call up the stairs, 'Hello, — is that you? Would you ever bring me down that book on the hall seat?' or some such thing, and there would be silence, frightening sometimes until you got used to it. I feel 'Horatio' (so named for some reason now forgotten) just likes this house, as we do, and has no intention of going away. I think he is the first man who laid out the back garden. I was told he planted the poplar and seven apple trees and two pear trees, and he built an apple house, so-called to this day, with shelves you can pull out to test for ripeness. 'Horatio' appears to be a nice man with a face similar to J. M. Synge's who just likes to make sure his house is not being abused.

The only people he ever seriously frightened were a party of teenagers taking advantage of a 'free house' a few years ago. The big sound of their generation was turned up full and I'm glad I was away. All the action was downstairs that night and the upper hall was in darkness. A girl on her way to the bathroom ('Horatio's' room, you will remember) heard the hall door opening and the footsteps and she called out, 'Who's that?' No answer, and she swears the empty hall was deathly cold in the middle of summer. She returned shaking to the party and begged some friends to accompany her on her next trip upstairs.

Several other young people were similarly frightened, even one member of this family, but that was only because 'Horatio' was annoyed by the awful noise! Why normally should we worry? You buy an old house in which people have lived and died for a hundred and fifty years, and if some decide to stay on, you have to remember that it was their home first. I think you have to be glad when they agree to share it.

11. An Irish Link with Tutankhamun

The tomb of the Pharaoh was discovered by pure accident in the Royal Valley of the Kings in Luxor, Egypt in 1922. The famous archaeologist Howard Carter and his patron, Lord Carnarvon, after ten years of unsuccessful excavating for the tomb had decided to give up the quest. As they had borrowed equipment from the British Army, a Sergeant Richard Adamson, a Yorshireman, was sent to make an inventory of them for their safe return. While doing this he lived in a tent in the bleak, lonely valley.

On the afternon of 3 November 1922, Adamson decided to take a stroll to the disused huts on top of Rameses' tomb. As he was returning, picking his way over crushed chippings, he heard a shout, and looking down saw a group of excited Arab workers gathered around a large hole about ten or twelve feet deep and talking to one another. They had uncovered about eight or nine large boulders. When they suddenly saw Adamson looking at them they hurriedly pushed the boulders into the hole and filled it in. He did not speak Arabic, so he returned to his tent, but the next morning he told Carter, who went to the spot. When the boulders and rubble were again removed, the steps that led down to the tomb of Tutankhamun were discovered, but it was to take two years of hard work before the actual chamber with the king's body was reached.

Shortly before all this there had been a strange

happening in Co. Tipperary. At the outbreak of the 1914-18 war, the famous clairvoyant and palmist, Count Louis Harmon, known as 'Cheiro' (Greek for a hand) had settled in Ireland. The tragic events of the rebellion made him decide to return to London, where he still had his consulting rooms, to read the hands of royalty and wealthy patrons.

Years before, an archaeologist friend had given him a mummified hand. The delicately shaped fingers and nails covered with gold leaf indicated that it was that of a woman. On the first finger was a gold ring, engraved with minute hieroglyphics. The archaeologist said the hand was that of Princess Makitaten, daughter of the Pharaoh Akhenaten. For thirty years Cheiro had kept the hand in a case, mounted on a cushion. As he and his wife were packing for their return to England he noticed that the hand appeared to have changed both in substance and colour. It seemed to be decomposing, so he decided that instead of packing it, the right thing to do would be to cremate it.

By a strange coincidence, the night was 31 October, Hallowe'en. They lit a small fire in one of the ground floor rooms and as Cheiro carried the ebony stand on which the hand was reposed into the room, his wife began reading the funeral service from the Egyptian *Book of the Dead*. Cheiro placed the complete stand, hand and all into the glowing fire. Soon bright flames shot up into the air, and there was an aroma of spices. When all was burned the couple decided to go to bed. As they ascended the stairs, their backs to the entrance hall, they felt a sudden rush of wind. They turned around, and as they did the heavy oak front door rattled.

The air became very cold and suddenly, with a crash, the heavy old door shot open. They could see out into the moonlit garden where an undefinable shape was moving towards the doorway. As it passed over the threshold it began to materialise. While Cheiro and his wife watched spellbound it assumed the upper portion of a beautiful woman, with a face full of nobility, grandeur and pride.

She wore what appeared to be a headdress, formed by the carved wings of beetles, the ends of which rested on her shoulders. In the centre of her forehead was the golden asp emblem of Egyptian royalty. She moved towards them, lifted her hands and bowed. Then moving backwards she slowly melted out the doorway into the moonlight outside.

In the morning Cheiro raked out the bones from among the ashes of the fire with the intention of returning them some day to where the hand had come from in Egypt. He found the gold ring intact.

Back in London, on the very evening of the day on which the story of the fabulous discovery of Tutankhamun's tomb was splashed all over the newspapers, Count Louis Harmon and his wife were sitting in their West End home. Suddenly the electric lights began to fade and the lamp on Cheiro's desk at which he was sitting sank to a dull red glow. The figure of the Egyptian princess again appeared, and this time her hand was pointing at the desk. Cheiro automatically grabbed his scribbling pad and began writing. In a few seconds the figure faded away and the lights returned to normal. He looked down at what he had written.

Lord Carnarvon not to enter tomb. Disobey at peril. If ignored would suffer sickness; not recover; death would claim him in Egypt.

Cheiro immediately wrote a letter to Lord Carnarvon, who had been one of his clients, telling him of this strange message.

However, possibly because Carnarvon was so excited over the find, he ignored the warning and with his daughter went into the tomb many times. Just after he had inspected the chamber in which the king's body reposed in a huge golden shrine, tragedy struck. As he walked up the steps into the open air he was stung on the cheek by a mosquito. The following morning as he was shaving, his razor slipped and he nicked the top of the spot. He had to go to bed with a high fever. Two days later he was up, apparently recovered. He visited the tomb site again, and shortly afterwards had a relapse. He was taken to hospital in Cairo and within a week he was in a serious condition. His wife had rushed to his bedside from England, and when his son and heir arrived from India, he found his father delirious.

That night Lord Carnavon died. Almost at the exact time the electric light failed mysteriously all over Cairo. For five minutes the city was in darkness. No logical reason was found for the failure. It was also learned later that Lord Carnarvon's pet dog thousands of miles away in his home in Wales had howled at the time of his death. When eventually, a long time afterwards, they uncovered the body of the king, they found that he had a mark on his face exactly where Lord Carnarvon had been bitten by the mosquito!

Shortly after Carnarvon had been laid to rest in his family vault in Wales, his son, the new Lord Carnarvon, received a telephone call from a lady. It was a medium, who said that his father had 'come through' with a message. 'He said that on no account were you to step inside the tomb of Tutankhamun again. Your father says that if you do so you will surely die and that would mean the end of the family line.' (He was unmarried at the time.)

The young Carnarvon promised he would never go near the tomb. Some weeks later the same lady rang again, and said his father had heard of the promise and was very pleased. He never heard from this lady again and never went into the tomb.

And why was Howard Carter not affected by the curse? Apparently he used to talk to the two figures (Kas) which guarded the burial chamber, which was supposed to contain the spirit of the Pharaoh until the time came for his soul to fly to the stars. He left these figures there until everything else was removed and promised to leave the actual body of the king in the chamber where it was found, and there it still reposes in its heavy stone coffin.

12. When Churchyards Yawn. . .

A respectable family in Drogheda, a handsome and hospitable town, who were friends to the drama, became known to all strangers who came on a visit. The mother, a few years before the theatre there opened, died and was buried. Being a woman of property, in her will she ordered that a valuable ring which she wore should be buried with her.

A servant in the family, being aware of this, made up his mind that so valuable a gem should not be lost to the world. So at the bewitching hour of night, when churchyards yawn, he stole stealthily along, opened the grave and coffin, and began his plunder.

But from evil at times comes good. In cutting the finger off the corpse to get possession of the ring, the lady revived, and said, 'John, what's the matter?'

John, terrified, without waiting to reply, fled from the churchyard, while the lady in her shroud, raised herself up, walked home, and knocked at the door, which was opened by her astonished husband.

This lady recovered, and lived for many years. I have seen her as she frequently visited the theatre. A short time ago, the London papers mentioned an aged lady's death in Drogheda, and alluded to the circumstances of the ring and her having been buried alive in her early days.

A tale similar to this has been often told, the locality being placed in another quarter; but it is an authenticated fact, well-known in Drogheda.

From **Fifty Years of Green Room Gossip** *by W. Donaldson.*

13. A Person Imprisoned in the Past

It was in a haunted house in a lonely part of Co. Dublin one Hallowe'en night, when the wind was howling outside, that I heard the following story. No ghosts appeared while I was there, but the conversation was so spooky that when I went out into the darkness to go home my imagination conjured up all sorts of apparitions.

The tale came from my hostess, a mine of information on the supernatural. Here it is exactly as she told it to me:

'One Christmas Eve many years ago, a woman friend of mine, a painter, decided after lunch to take her sketch book and to go around Dublin to get some inspiration, knowing the streets would not be as crowded as usual. She wandered around the old areas in the vicinity of Christchurch, noting anything that took her fancy.

'Eventually she crossed the Liffey at Winetavern Street Bridge, ambled along the North Quays, cutting through the Ormond Market and into Mary's Abbey. I might add that she didn't know the locality, and as she was from the country didn't know much about the city's history. Crossing the street she saw a tiny alleyway, and went over to it. The place was quiet and deserted at the time. Almost hidden away at the right-hand side was a large doorway, partly open.

'Filled with curiosity she pulled back the door, and found herself looking into what appeared to be a very old building (the light wasn't too good and it was approaching dusk at the time). There were steps inside and she descended to a lower floor. She was delighted to see a fine vaulted roof as well as corner stones and stone carvings. It was while she was inspecting a detail at the far corner of the building that she heard a sound. As she turned around there was a loud crash, and the sound of a key turning. To her horror she realised she had been locked in! She ran as fast as she could up the steps, shouting, but by this time the caretaker had turned the corner out of earshot. She banged and shouted to no avail. She was a prisoner.

'Being a level-headed woman she calmly took stock of her situation, and wrapping her coat around herself, sat down on the bare floor, hoping to hear someone passing by, but as it was a cul-de-sac and only used for storage, this was most unlikely. Apart from noisy revellers in the distance, she heard no one, and in the darkness she lost all sense of time, but tried to keep her senses by reciting snatches of poetry and singing songs, dozing off from time to time.

'It must have been St Stephen's Day, as she afterwards recalled, that she appeared to become delirious. She said the place suddenly lit up like daylight, and at the end of the large and by this time gaily decorated building, she was amazed to see a big open doorway. She walked up to it and found herself outside in brilliant sunshine. Birds were singing and there were strange buildings, beautiful trees and flowers for miles around. In the distance she could see the river moving along slowly through green fields. She was aware of monk-like figures moving about, but she could not see their faces.

'The vision, if such it was, lasted for some time, and then she awoke to find herself cramped, cold and in darkness again. Her ordeal came to an end the following day when her feeble cries were heard by men returning to work after Christmas. The place was opened up and she was taken to hospital for treatment. It was many months before she was back to normal again and up to the present day she doesn't know whether she was dreaming, or whether in some strange way she was transported for a time back several hundred years.

The place where this adventure happened is the Chapter House of St Mary's Abbey, where in 1534 Silken Thomas, son of Garret Mor Fitzgerald the Earl of Kildare, hearing a rumour that his father had been executed in London, burst in with his followers and flung down the Sword of State (his father had been Lord Deputy) and started the rebellion which cost him his life.

The Chapter House is the only intact part of the Cistercian Abbey, which was closed at the Reformation, left today.

14. Lord Mountnugent's Battle with the Devil

About three miles outside the town of Roscrea, over the border into Offaly, lies Mount St Joseph's Cistercian Monastery. Through a tall gateway whose pillars are mounted by two brazen eagles, a long driveway leads up to the guest house, which was formerly the castle of Lord Mountnugent. A few hundred yards from the castle is the graveyard hidden from view by pine trees.

Lord Mountnugent was a lonely sort of man, spending most of his time attending to his estate of about 1,500 acres, and sitting by his fireside where he would often spend most of the night. As a result of this, the local people used to spread strange stories about the old man, saying that he was up colloguing with the devil.

One afternoon Lord Mountnugent returned home after a tour of his estate. He walked slowly to the front door and having just pulled at the bell handle fell heavily to the ground. One of the servants opened the door and let out a scream that brought the rest of the household running to the hallway. Lord Mountnugent was lifted gently and placed upon a couch and a doctor was sent for.

After about ten minutes, Lord Mountnugent opened his eyes and called to his chief steward, asking him to tell the workers to bring all the farm stock to the front of the house. While this was being done he also asked that the couch be placed at a window overlooking these proceedings.

After a while an old grey horse, with bony hooves and a shaggy coat, could be seen coming towards the front of the house, followed by cattle and all other forms of farm animals. It was twilight when the last of them arrived.

The servant looking after Lord Mountnugent went to the kitchen to get him a drink. As she closed the door behind her, the old gun-dog which was lying on the ground beside his master got up and let out a long howl. Immediately after, a crash like breaking furniture was heard reverberating all over the house. Outside the sky darkened and a strong wind sprang up. All the animals fled down the drive-way just as the doctor was arriving. His carriage was bowled over and he landed in a hedge. The old grey horse was the last to leave.

When the servants rushed to the front door they found it locked. The men set about breaking down the door and they had just done so when the doctor came in. Lord Mountnugent was lying peacefully on his couch and he was holding a small cross in his hand. He was dead. The dog was also dead with a splinter of wood from a piece of furniture through his heart. There was a smell like burning in the room.

The following morning all the animals came back, led by the old grey horse. The house was closed up, and Lord Mountnugent was buried on his own land, with a few relations and retainers at the funeral.

Local people in the area say he had a battle with the devil and won.

Now the house is a place of pilgrimage and rest and is overshadowed by a church. It is said, however, that some nights during the year a hazy ball of light is seen to leave the graveyard where Lord Mountnugent lies buried and to hang by the outside wall, inside of which his portrait once hung. It stays for some moments and then fades away.

This story was told to me by Brendan Price of Dublin

15. Ghostly Monks

The following adventure befell my friend, Mr Larry O'Carroll of Walkinstown, Co. Dublin, a keen fisherman. He told me that on 28 October some years back he motored south on a fishing trip with two friends, Bob and Harry.

'We stopped at Cloghane, Co. Kerry, about three o'clock and decided to have a drink. While doing so we asked the local friendly publican did he know of anywhere we could stay for bed and breakfast.

'He replied that it was almost impossible to find accommodation at that time of the year as the fishing was so good, but we might be alright if we continued on to Tralee. We said however that we thought that was a bit too far.

'He thought for a moment and said: "If you want to take a chance I might be able to get the key of a particular house, and if you stay more than one night perhaps you might give a small donation at the end of the week."

'It sounded somewhat sinister and we expected a sort of gloomy old place but having arrived there we were surprised to find it was a modern, brand-new house, only two years old, in fact with all modern conveniences.

'Having left our cases we went off fishing over the Conor Pass to Inch. We arrived back at the pub about ten o'clock and after refreshment found our way back to our new residence.

'As soon as we went in and put on all the lights,

some of the upstairs ones went out for no apparent reason. After supper we adjourned to our respective rooms — my friends in a room with two single beds and myself in a double-bedded room, one of those in which the lights had failed.

'Our doors faced each other at the top of the stairs and outside there was a corridor which went past four bedrooms, two on each side, ending in a cul-de-sac. Before retiring I checked that all the doors below were locked. It was a warm and very stormy night.

'At exactly half past six next morning I awoke to find the temperature had dropped to below zero, and my friends awoke at the same time with the intense cold. We all looked out into the passage, and the three of us at the same time saw gliding along a tall figure with long black sleeky hair, wearing either a habit or a robe dark in colour, looking like a monk of hundreds of years ago.

'I reached the door first and collided with my friends, who appeared very shaken and shocked, and Bob just pointed to the end bedroom on the right. All three of us made our way to this particular room where the door was open, and we rushed in together to find no sign of our mysterious visitor.

'Later that morning we called to the publican who met us at the door, and he knowingly said: "You've all apparently had a very disturbed night."

'He informed us after a lot of persuasion that the house where we had stayed had originally been a quarry and tradition had it that strange things had happened there in years gone by. A gallows, he said, had been erected there on which many people had been executed for trivial offences.

'That evening when we arrived back from fishing, one of the lads in the pub turned on the televison. *The Riordans* came on and the programme involved a ghost. The following day, Monday, after a heavy day's fishing we arrived back at our house at exactly eleven o'clock, switched on the television and we heard the following words: "And now here is tonight's ghost story!"'

16. Strange Goings-On in County Mayo

In his book, *Between Two Worlds,* the late Captain Dermott MacManus tells of the haunting of his ancestral home, Killeaden House, Kiltimagh, Co. Mayo.

At the time of the hauntings Captain MacManus's two maiden aunts, Emma and Lottie, were living in the big house in Killeaden, the former sleeping in the front upstairs room to the left of the hall and the latter in the adjoining rooms at the back. It was decided to take up the large ancient flagstone in the hallway and re-lay the floor.

When this work was started a 'strange brooding atmosphere' seemed to settle on the house. At night heavy iron-shod steps were heard tramping up and down the hall, accompanied by the ringing and clinking of metal, as if made by heavy old-fashioned spurs or sword and scabbard.

This would continue for minutes or sometimes up to half an hour. The dog was nearly driven frantic with terror, but the two ladies were more indignant at having their rest spoiled, than frightened.

A clergyman was called in but his exorcism failed to stop the activities of the spirit until one night they heard the stamping noises heavier and angrier than ever. Captain MacManus writes: 'After twenty minutes the steps stopped, but only for a few minutes. . . this time they began to climb the stairs, getting nearer and near to the defenceless women above. . . they moved along the landing, stopped for a moment and then moved towards my aunt's bedroom door.

'The door began to open slowly, although my aunt had locked it earlier. Emma watched with surprise and horror but then pulled herself together and in a loud voice cried out: "I forbid you to enter." Three times she said this and on each occasion the door stopped moving for a few seconds and then started again. The struggle of wills continued, and Emma sitting up straight in bed, facing the door, fiercely cried: "In the name of the Holy Trinity and by the Divine Power of God, I command you, Go!" Three times she said this adding at the last, "Go I command you, and rest in the peace which only God can give."

'Then as my Aunt Lottie listened in the other room there was a slam that rang through the old house and made the windows rattle. . . the door jerked shut and the steps went slowly down, until they reached the centre of the hall and ceased, never to be heard again.

'The following morning the workmen digging under the flagstones in the hall came upon human bones. These later were identified as those of a young woman and a baby. The mystery of how they came to be there was never solved, but the haunting has ceased for ever.'

17. The Girl with the High Heels

Some reputable friends of Tomás Bairead told him that a woman or girl wearing high heels walked down the road outside his house in his home town in Connemara every night at one o'clock in the morning going in the direction of the churchyard. 'I didn't pay much attention to them until one night I heard the footsteps coming down the road. I looked at my watch — one o'clock exactly. Only for the other people I wouldn't have paid any attention to them.

'Many nights after that I heard her, at the same time: the same kind of walk, click of the high heels, and going in the same direction. I never heard her coming back, and I never stayed awake long enough, although often I awakened before she went past the doorway. She was better than any clock in Ireland. One night when my watch stopped at eleven o'clock. I fixed it by her passing, and sure enough it was perfectly correct next morning.

'I heard her pass on a night that one wouldn't put a dog outside in; one autumn night when there was a very heavy shower that kept me awake, I heard her pass just before the torrents came, and she went at the same pace as usual. We eventually called her the "Girl of the Churchyard".

'A man at the other side of the churchyard said he never heard her — but no one knew of any girl out at that hour of night, winter or summer. One night, coming home from a wake, I had barely closed my gate when my hair raised like a dog's coat bristling for no reason at all, for I neither heard nor saw anything, and I wasn't feeling afraid!

'Just as I was putting the key in the door I heard the woman's footsteps forty or fifty feet down the street. At first I thought it was someone else coming from the wake, but they all lived in the opposite direction. When I got inside the house it was just after one o'clock. No one saw the girl; it was only her steps were heard, and after the 1916 Rising she was never heard again. It was thought she may have been killed on the roadway in that area.'

Tomás also tells of a man going in a cart for provisions to Moycullen when the horse stopped suddenly on a lonely road surrounded by trees. Having forced the animal on, he came upon a tall man, smoking a pipe. From his clothes and appearance he recognised him as a neighbour who had died some time previously. A sort of mist seemed to envelop the area, and it was a long time before he got clear of it and out into the light again. He didn't recover from the ordeal for some days.

He talks about the old tradition that the small animals, the stoats, have a funeral when one of their members die, and claims he saw twenty or thirty of them once in a procession across a field.

Regarding the Hungry Grass (which, if trodden on, will cause terrible gnawing hunger pains) he said: 'One sunny summer afternoon after a meal I went for a walk and when about four miles outside the town I suddenly felt strange. It wasn't so much a feeling of hunger as a weakness. My feet went from under me and I broke out in a sweat. It was a struggle to make my way home, and when I got there I fell into bed. I wasn't well again for about three days.'

Finally, he tells us that when, about 1950, they were rebuilding the old church in Moycullen he heard that the body of a fourteen-year-old girl buried about fifteen years previously had been unearthed, and she was found to be in a perfect state of preservation, even to the ribbon on her hair. She was put into a new coffin and buried again.

The late Tomás Bairead in his autobiography called **Gan Baisteadh** *included many stories of the supernatural.*

18. A Rector who comes back

I was told of an authentic case of haunting in connection with the medieval church of St Audeon's near the Old City Gate in Cook Street, Dublin. It takes the form of an apparition of the old rector of sixty years ago, a popular and revered figure in the district.

The apparition was seen by at least three people. On one occasion, a young clergyman in the pulpit faltered in his sermon and finally concluded his discourse in an almost incoherent manner. A lady who was present in the congregation that morning distinctly saw the robed figure hovering behind the young parson in the pulpit, as if listening critically to him.

He was clearly outlined against the stained glass window behind the pulpit for some minutes. After the sermon, she related her queer experience to the young preacher, who expressed no surprise. 'Something told me not to turn around,' he explained. 'That is why I was unable to concentrate on my carefully prepared sermon.' The young clergyman was in normal circumstances a gifted speaker.

The old rector in his somewhat old-fashioned outdoor garb was also seen by a resident of High Street, on his way leisurely to the old church on a warm summer's night. A recent rector was working at church accounts late one night, when he heard the well-remembered distinctive footfalls of the old rector in the church beyond. He quickly ended his labours and left the vestry, but saw nothing.

19. A Dreadful Experience

Aiden Grennell came down to the theatre one evening in a terrible state. He said he had had a dreadful experience. This was before he was married, when he was living in digs in Lower Mount Street, Dublin.

In his bedroom there were two beds, one of which was usually empty. After the evening show he found that the landlady had let the other bed to someone else. She was entitled to, and Aiden could make no complaint. The man was asleep anyway, so there was nothing to do but go to bed himself.

At three o'clock in the morning the stranger in the other bed began to groan. Tragic dying groans, groans to put the heart across you. Aiden switched on the light to see what could be done. As he looked at the sleeping man moaning convulsively a shadow began to form over this stranger's diaphragm and gradually grew larger until it turned into an old woman with grey straggling locks who muttered and wept woefully, wringing her hands. She gradually moved behind the bed and disappeared into the shadows by the wardrobe. Needless to say Aiden stayed under the bed-clothes shivering and shaking for the rest of the night.

He came down to the theatre that evening in quite a state and we told him to throw Holy Water at the stranger, as that might keep him quiet or even save him from whatever was troubling him. We hadn't any to give him that evening so Aiden had to face another night without it.

Punctual to the minute at three o'clock the groans began again and the shadow started to emerge, but Aiden stayed under the bed-clothes after that.

We gave him a bottle of Holy Water and he said that he would sprinkle the man with it. As soon as the groans began Aiden jumped up and threw Holy Water over the stranger with quite a splash. All groans ceased immediately. The man's convulsions ceased and he dropped off into a child-like and calm sleep. The next night the man was moved to another room but Aiden heard him screaming in the early hours of the morning.

20. Banshee

A banshee usually presages a death in the family. And some families are regularly followed by them. Anyone with an 'O' in front of their name is liable to be followed! Maybe by mournful wailing or screams or by a black dog or by a multitude of foxes.

At Coolbawn on the shores of Lough Derg in Co. Tipperary lived the Bruce sisters, famous for good works and officials of the St John Ambulance Brigade. They were various aunts and the mother of Tyrrell Pine, an actor at the Gate Theatre and a composer of music. Bertie Bruce, his youngest aunt, was making a fire for a picnic by the lake-shore while the others were out fishing. The fire was in an enclosed spot bounded by the lake on one side and two impassable hedges on the other.

Bertie had just turned away for a moment to collect some wood when she looked back to the fire and there was an old lady in rags leaning over it. Bertie went up to her and offered her bread, but she muttered incomprehensibly and would not take it so Bertie went back to collect more faggots. She glanced back to the fire. The old woman had totally disappeared! How had she gone with no one seeing her? How had she got there? There was no way. And later the others who were out in the boat said they had seen no one.

It turned out afterwards that a member of the family had died at that moment in a house nearby. They were known to be followed by a banshee.

Certain unknown vibrations at death might perhaps be picked up by sensitive souls and translated into their own imagery of old women, dogs, little men, or wails and moans. If ever I ask a class that I have been teaching whether anyone has experienced a banshee, usually someone admits to something of the kind.

These two stories were told to me by Christopher Casson

21. Steptoe's Ghostly Experience

Albert Steptoe is probably one of the best known and most popular characters on television, so much so that Wilfrid Brambell, the actor who plays the part, can now be hardly imagined in any other rôle.

Yet Wilfrid, who was born in Dublin, was one of the most talented actors in his native city. I remember vividly his wonderful Sir Andrew Aguecheek in a Longford Players production of *Twelfth Night* and a poignant portrayal of the English chaplain in Shaw's *Saint Joan*. On another occasion, he took over Jimmy O'Dea's role in a pantomime with great success. Afterwards he made a name for himself on the London stage. Recently he published his autobiography, *All Above Board,* and as everyone has at least one ghost story I was not surprised to find that he also had one.

In 1956, he had changed to a new home in Swiss Cottage on the outskirts of London.

'There were five attic rooms on top of Miss Wier's semi-detached and uninhabited residence. Miss Wier was the rich and frustrated spinster daughter of a tea planter, and whilst accepting my rent, closed her eyes to and denied the fact that she was any form of landlady. She locked and bolted her hall door regularly every evening at eleven, coolly ignoring my protestations that my curtain in the West End did not come down until a quarter to eleven.

'With clockwork regularity, she locked herself in and me out. She was in the habit, in her loneliness, of

110

spending three months' holiday abroad annually, trying to enjoy herself. I enjoyed her absence.

'At great expense at that time, I had saved up for
and bought myself a record player and two records,
which in Miss Wier's absence I played incessantly.

'One Sunday morning, during my ear-splitting
ecstasy, I noticed from my room, four floors up, a
young man standing in the next-door back garden
with his head back, his feet apart and his thumbs
stuck into the waistband of his trousers. I could not
see his expression, but in fear that it was one of
discontent, I poked my head through my already
wide-open window and roared: "Is it too loud?" To
which he replied: "No! Not loud enough."

'Obligingly, I increased the volume and thereafter
I made a friend of my neighbour. Barry is Polish and
the husband of that international pianist, Joyce
Hatto, the only Hampshire girl to have been officially
invited to play Chopin in Warsaw. She is a very pretty
and unaffected musician.

'Before she left for Warsaw for her three-week
engagement she told me that her husband was returning home four days before her and would I please
keep him company during that interim. He assured
me that he would immediately ring my bell on his
arrival home next door the following Monday.

'At two o'clock on the following Sunday I was
working on my current script in Miss Wier's empty
house when my concentration was broken by a far
too loud long-playing record from the living room
next door. I accepted the fact that Barry had made an
early return. Next morning when he rang my bell and
invited me to join him in his flat for a "cuppa", I

asked him why he had not done so the previous night. He told me that he had landed only one hour previously at Heathrow Airport.

'"But," I said, "why was your record player at full volume at two o'clock last night?" After a pause, he tentatively asked me if the music which I so loudly had heard was *The Norwegian Lament*. It was, and when I told him so he said, "I thought so, it often happens."

'"The Victorian terraced house must have been haunted by two spirits who still do not know that they are dead. . . Frequently in the twilight hours," he added, "the kitchen light was switched on, and, shadowed on the open kitchen door bending over the kitchen stove, were the figures of a loving couple preparing an evening meal together prior to switching on their ever-repeated melody." I heard the music on several occasions afterwards, but the subject was never again broached.'